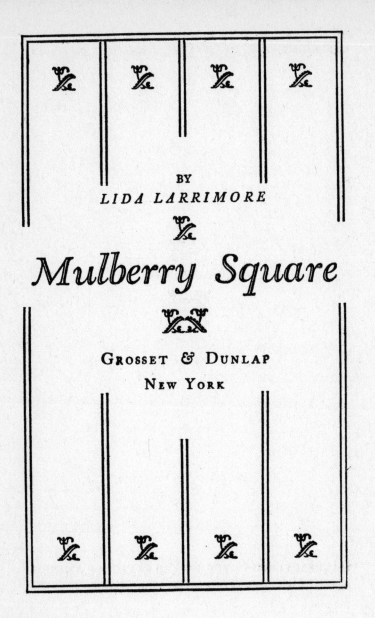

BY
LIDA LARRIMORE

Mulberry Square

GROSSET & DUNLAP
NEW YORK

Part One

Mulberry Square

I

I

"THERE were four mulberry trees. They grew around the fountain in the center of the Square. Their leaves were rough and heart-shaped and when it was ripe the purple fruit dropped of its own accord into the grass. The . . ."

"Janie!"

That was Mother calling from downstairs. Janie sat very still and almost held her breath. If she didn't answer, perhaps Mother would think she had gone out somewhere. She smiled, thinking how, at nineteen, the subterfuges of her childhood still clung. Silence! No sound but the wind in the locusts and a hand-organ playing in the Square . . . "My wild Irish rose, The sweetest flower that grows" . . . No sound from Mother. Janie drew a long deep breath and dipped her pen in the ink well.

"The mulberry trees were very old. There was a legend about them. One of the early settlers, a certain Sir Godfrey Ballard, from whom our family is descended ——"

That sounded like bragging. If it was accepted, Professor Vail might read it aloud to the class. Every one would think she was putting on airs. Janie hesitated. Well, it was a little like wearing a D.A.R. emblem pinned outside of your coat. She drew her pen through the clause and continued.

"—— brought them from his English garden to grow in the virgin soil of New Kingston, then a tiny settlement on the banks of the Delaware."

Janie's grave little pointed face, bending intently over the paper, wore a pleased expression. That sounded very well, she thought—especially the "Virgin soil." Not much virgin soil left in this part of New Kingston now, if virgin meant pure and undefiled. The mills made everything grimy. Her eyes, hazel eyes, spaced wide apart under brows like slender wings, lifted from the "theme," strayed out through the window and down into the Square. Little girls were playing house under the mulberry trees as she and Celia and Muriel had played there a very long time ago. Janie and Celia and Muriel . . . "Good afternoon, Mrs. Morningstar. We thought we would come for tea" . . . Janie and

Celia and Muriel. Cleaner than the little girls who played there now. Starched white petticoats, sashes, slippers tied with bows. Muriel's governess watching them from a nearby bench. Joseph bringing the pony cart. Janie and Celia and Muriel. Sailing boats in the fountain . . .

"Janie!"

Mother again. Another interval of waiting. Another long sigh of relief. Janie's attention returned to the "theme."

"It is said ——" She crossed that out and substituted—"Sir Godfrey Ballard, so runs the legend, grew them from cuttings taken from a mulberry tree in Shakespeare's garden at Stratford." There. That should make an impression on Professor Vail. Perhaps it was true. Great-aunt Rose said it was and she had been to England. Great-aunt Rose doted on ancestors. Great-uncle Charlie, who was her brother, said she would have them all descended from Rameses the Second only he was a colored man . . .

How fragrant the locust blossoms were! Like lilies on Easter Sunday. It must be dull for Celia at the shore with Great-aunt Rose. Lovely to smell the ocean, though, and watch the waves curve up in scallops on the sand. Lilies made you think of Celia. White and gold. "Little Saint Cecelia!" Rats! . . .

"JANIE!"

Very loud this time. Coming closer. Footsteps

climbing the third floor stairs. Janie began to scrib-
ble with furious haste . . . "Rats—Rats—Rats.
Three blind mice. See how they run" . . . Shin-
gled brown head bent over the table. Jaws set.
Forehead wrinkled into a frown. Ink on her nose
and her fingertips. A lady absorbed in literary
efforts and lost to the world outside.

Mother opened the door.

"Janie!" she said reproachfully. "I've called you
half a dozen times."

Janie glanced up.

"Did you?" There. That wasn't exactly a fib.

"What in the world are you doing?"

"Writing a theme. If it's good enough, I may
get into Professor Vail's short-story class next year."

"That's splendid, dear." The reproach changed
into enthusiasm. Mother wanted Janie to write.
Since she wasn't pretty like Celia, she had to do
something of the kind. "What is the topic?"
Mother was beaming. "What are you writing
about?"

"The Square."

"Well for Heaven's sake!" Mother no longer
was beaming. "I should think you could find a
more interesting subject than that."

"But it is interesting, Mother." Janie's words
tumbled over each other in their haste to get themselves spoken. "It's been here since before the
Revolutionary War and there have been so many
changes and it's so different now and——"

"I should say it is!"

Janie's enthusiasm wilted like a pricked balloon. You couldn't make Mother understand. She hated the Square now that everybody who mattered at all had moved out to Manor street and Delaware Heights. Well, Father would understand. Janie brightened a little. She would tell him about it to-night . . .

"Going somewhere?" she asked, noticing that Mother wore her second-best hat with roses around the brim.

"I want to get the material for Celia's dress." Mother was drawing on white silk gloves a little yellowed from washing. "The sample was in her letter. That's why I called you. Do you know where it is?"

"Here, I think." Janie pulled open the drawer of her writing table. Yes, there it was. Celia's dainty handwriting on a hotel envelope . . . Haddon Hall . . . That was a pretty name . . . Dorothy Vernon of Haddon Hall . . . In England they made cider out of apples mixed with mulberry juice . . .

"Hurry, dear! Is the sample inside?"

Janie produced the precious scrap and Mother tucked it inside her bag.

"It's probably all gone now," she said with a plaintive sigh. "Such a lovely shade of lilac!"

Janie smiled to herself. Mother always worried about things like that. She was sure the cream was sour before she tasted it, that the pipes would burst next winter and that every unopened letter contained distressing news. It was remarkable, she thought, that Mother had managed to keep her youthful prettiness in spite of such mountains of worry. She was plump, in a dainty fashion, and not much taller than Janie. Her skin was smooth and fair. There were few threads of gray in her wavy light brown hair. Her eyes were the high lovely blue of a picture post card lake and seldom shadowed with real anxiety. Worrying, with Mother, Janie decided, was merely a habit, like putting on your left stocking first and picking up pins in the street.

"I hate to walk up town." Mother was looking at herself in Janie's mirror. "The sun is so hot."

"Don't go then," Janie advised . . . No, Mother didn't worry inside. She was preening herself like a pretty pigeon . . .

"But I promised Celia I'd send her another dress."

"She isn't exactly in rags and tatters." Janie remembered the bags and the shiny new hat box. "She should be able to manage."

"You don't understand, dear." Mother's blue eyes were reproachful. "Celia is sensitive. She can't take too many favors from dear Aunt Rose."

"Rats!" said Janie—but not out loud.

"It's hard for her to be dependent." Mother powdered her nose. "And she's always so brave about it. Celia," she added tenderly, "has a beautiful disposition."

Janie made no comment. Celia's courage was a family myth. So was her sweet disposition. There were other myths about Celia. Celia was delicate. Celia was a martyr to circumstances. Celia, in a setting more glamorous than Mulberry Square, could marry any one she pleased. Mother believed all the Celia myths. Useless to argue. It only provoked a scene. Janie changed the subject.

"There are some French silk flowers in Leland's window marked less than half price," she said. "You wanted one for Celia's dress."

Mother remembered her errands uptown.

"It is hot, isn't it?" She picked up her bag and her flowered silk parasol. "I hate the belt-line trolley. If only I had a car of my own."

"I'll go for you," Janie offered.

"No thank you, dear." Mother's tone indicated that the mission was too important to be entrusted to Janie. "There's a sale at Allen's. I might be able to pick up something or other."

Janie did not insist. Mother, she knew, liked shopping and sales. In the stores she was almost sure to meet somebody who would tell her how clever she was to make Celia's dresses or how pretty Celia looked at the last club dance. Mother liked that. She wore such bits of praise like medals pinned on her chest.

"There are wicker porch sets in the sale at Al-

len's. Goodness knows we need one." Mother
considered a moment, her lower lip caught in her
teeth. "I might get it on installments."

"Father hates installments," Janie reminded her.
"You promised him Mother."

"Father has no idea how dreadful it is to be
shabby." Mother's voice was sharp. "Sometimes
I think he doesn't care about us at all."

Janie set her lips. She adored Father. It was
hard to hear Mother pick at him without flaming
to his defence. But what was the use? There were
myths about Father which Mother also firmly believed. Father might have been a famous surgeon.
Father was foolish to bury himself in Mulberry
Square. Father cared more about the foreigners
and the poor white trash in Vine and Juniper streets
than he did for his own dear children. Mother
believed those things. No use to argue. Nothing
to do but change the subject again.

"The forget-me-nots were darling," she said. "I
think Celia would like them best."

"They'll probably be gone by the time I get
there," Mother said merely from force of habit.
"Help Rachel with dinner, Janie, if I'm not back
by five. This is her lodge-meeting night. She's as
cross as a bundle of sticks."

Mother disappeared in a flutter of flowered voile.
Her slim high heels tapped sharply on the stairs. A
scent of violet perfume lingered for a moment on
the air, grew fainter, vanished completely. Pres-

ently the front door closed. Janie looked down
from the window. Mother crossed the street and
entered the Square. She walked as though the brick
paths might spoil her dainty slippers. A disdainful
lady with a flowered silk parasol. Out of place in
the shabby friendly old Square.

The afternoon was a little spoiled. Janie lost
her interest in the "theme." She sat looking down
into the Square. It *was* dingy and down at the
heel. The benches, shaded by locust and maple
trees, needed a coat of new green paint very badly.
The lamp posts staggered like tipsy old men with
their lantern-top hats askew. The nymphs on the
fountain had lost, here and there, a finger, an ear
or a nose. Once it had been lovely . . . Janie and
Celia and Muriel . . . Muriel would be coming
back soon. She'd probably be too grand to remember her poor relations in Mulberry Square . . .

Janie crossed to the mirror. Strange that people
always called her "plain." Horrid word! She
wasn't really so bad. Eyes sort of nice. Chestnut
hair that dipped in a peak on her forehead. Brown-
ish skin with pink underneath. Sort of solemn looking. But she did have a lovely smile. Everybody
said that. Too small ever to be queenly or wear a
bridesmaid's hat. Not so bad though. Only Celia
was so beautiful . . .

The ink didn't help any. She cold-creamed it off
and powdered her nose. She used a lip stick lightly.
Nice to be beautiful. Pleasant to know you can

marry anybody you please . . . "Bobby Shaftoe's
gone to sea. Silver buckles on his knee" . . . Now
what made her think of that? It didn't matter any
longer. She was nineteen years old and grown up
past "Mother Goose." Celia was twenty-one. She
would marry somebody pretty soon. Maybe
then . . .

"Janie!"

That was Father!

II

"Thank you, dear." Father was washing his
hands at the bowl in the office. "Did you mind
very much?"

"No." That was a fib. Janie's knees were shaking. Her stomach felt empty and queer. The
smell of ether always made her sick. But her hand
had been steady. Father didn't know. "Will he
be all right?" Poor Tony Silver. Beads of sweat
on his forehead . . .

"Of course. If he doesn't try to walk on it."
Father was packing fresh rolls of gauze into his
bag. "I suppose though," he added, "you can't afford the luxury of a broken leg if you have ten
children to feed."

"Are you going out again?"

Father's eyes were tired. He ought not to work
so hard. His shoulders were stooped and his hair
was almost entirely white. He looked twenty years

older than Mother instead of only just ten. "Why don't you stay home and rest?"

"Can't, baby." He paused on his way to the door and put his arm around Janie. "I appreciate your helping me out. Feel in my pocket," he said.

Janie found a paper bag and investigated its contents.

"Gum drops!" A lump crept into her throat. Father was never too busy to remember the things that she liked.

"So long as you stick to gum drops."

"Father! That's a pun!"

"Sorry. What I was going to say ——" He tilted her chin and smiled down into her eyes. "When your taste turns to French bon-bons, you'll have to find a wealthier beau."

"I'll always love you best."

"Nonsense. You don't mean that." His voice was very gentle. "But I like to hear it, of course. Now off with you and your gum drops. I've got to be on my way."

The office door closed. Outside a car spluttered and rattled into motion. Father was off on an errand of mercy with his shabby kit bag, his unending patience, his ready heart-warming smile.

Janie walked from the office into the hall, through the living-room and out on the shady side porch. She felt better now. The fragrance of mock-orange blossoms banished the ether smell. She lay in the hammock propped up against a heap of cushions.

There was a book on the bamboo table. She opened it and began to read. One small foot in a stub-toed sandal pushed against the floor to sway the hammock. One small hand dipped occasionally into the paper sack of gum drops. Worries forgotten, Janie read on and on.

Presently the words seemed jumbled and confused. Janie's eyelids began to droop. The sun was sinking in a luminous copper-gold glow. Insects buzzed in the wisteria vines. Somewhere at the back of the house Rachel was singing a camp meeting hymn. The book slid off onto the floor. The hammock swayed ever more slowly. Janie's lashes fluttered down against her cheeks. She sighed softly and slipped over the border into the drowsy country of dreams.

Footsteps aroused her, how much later she did not know. They came around the side of the house, thudding dully on the worn brick walk. Janie's eyelids were weighted with lead. Lifting them required a tremendous effort. She decided just to wait. The footsteps came nearer, halted for a moment, seemed to be walking towards her up the side porch steps. A voice said, "Good-afternoon."

It was a man's voice, low and pleasant and ever so faintly amused. Moreover, it was entirely unfamiliar. Janie opened her eyes.

A young man was standing on the top porch step holding his hat in his hands. Janie noticed his hair first of all. It seemed to match the sunlight, as though somebody had traced his head with a pencil against the copper-gold glow. As for the rest, her first impression was a sleepy jumble of broad tweed shoulders, brown eyes, sunburn, a nose that was just a nose, a wide mouth, a square sort of chin and a golden-brown necktie that looked expensive. Janie jerked up from the cushions as though someone had pulled an invisible string.

"This is Doctor Ballard's residence, isn't it?" he asked.

Janie nodded.

"Is the doctor at home?"

"Not now," she answered, "and the office door is around at the other side."

"I'm not a patient." He smiled down at the small grave person in the hammock. Her hair was tousled. Her cheeks were flushed. She looked, though she did not know it, very sleepy and cross and just about twelve years old. "I'm Hugh Kennedy," he said, as though the name might serve as a passport into any small person's esteem.

It did. Janie glanced with new interest at this smiling young man.

"Oh," she said. "You're Father's legacy."

"You might call me that, I suppose." He continued to smile. It crinkled his eyes and made them friendly. Janie approved of his eyes.

"We do," she confessed. "Just in the family, of course."

"I wrote Doctor Ballard. Doesn't he expect me?"

"Father is careless about letters," Janie explained. "It's probably in on his office desk under a book about bones, a couple of bills from the plumber and the Saturday Evening Post. Sit down," she added, remembering her manners.

"Thank you." He settled himself into a rocker beside the hammock. "Are you Doctor Ballard's little girl?"

"I'm Janie," she answered, "and almost entirely grown up."

"How grown up? Older than twelve and a half?"

"I'm a Moral Influence," she said to impress this smiling young man. "I keep little boys from breaking windows and shooting craps."

She saw that she had succeeded. He looked impressed and even somewhat startled.

"Not a lady policeman, by any chance?"

"Oh, no." Janie looked up at him gravely, not because she felt solemn but because her expression was made that way. "I'm the Assistant Director of the Community Playground."

"That's a large title for a small person."

"Isn't it?" Janie agreed. "And I've finished my first year in college. I only wear socks because it is stylish just now."

"I beg your pardon," he apologized. "I thought you were a child."

"People do." Janie sighed plaintively. "I had to produce a birth certificate before they would give me the playground job even though I've lived here all my life. And the policeman down there is always getting me mixed up with the urchins. It makes life very difficult."

He laughed at that. His teeth were even and very white. Viewed singly, as they emerged from the sleepy jumble, his features were not unattractive. His hair, Janie decided, just escaped being red. His mouth quirked humorously at the corners. He wasn't exactly handsome but he looked like somebody it would be pleasant to know. She began to enjoy herself. She was so seldom permitted to occupy the center of the stage. Celia saw to that. But Celia, thanks to dear Aunt Rose, was safely out of the way. Janie became expansive.

"Actually meeting you," she said, "is like seeing the Prince of Wales or Billy Sunday or —— You know, somebody you've heard of all your life but never expected to behold with your very own eyes."

"You knew I was coming some time." He smiled as though he, too, was having a very nice time. "You must have known that if you knew about me at all."

"Of course. But it was all so indefinite. Father never told us much about it except that your Father had asked him to let you work here as his assistant when you finished at the hospital. And then later there was a letter from a lawyer in New York."

"It's legal all right," he said a bit grimly. "My sister Louise did her best but it wasn't any use."

"Didn't she want you to come?"

"She wept over me as though I had been sentenced to prison."

Janie bridled.

"New Kingston isn't as bad as that. Or even Mulberry Square."

"I'm sure it isn't." He shrugged his shoulders. "Anyway, I'm here to stay for a year."

"Father needs somebody," Janie said gravely. "He works too hard all the time."

"He's splendid." Young Doctor Kennedy's voice sounded warm and sincere. "He came for commencement when I graduated from Jeff. He and my Dad were classmates, you know. Dad was pretty fine, too. He died eight years ago. I never knew exactly why he wanted me to come here except that he admired Doctor Ballard and always said he was a credit to the profession."

Janie fairly glowed. Praise for Father made her feel happy inside. Her liking for Father's young doctor increased with a sudden bound.

"Have you come this time to stay?"

"Bag and baggage. It's piled at the office door. I hadn't the energy to lug it around this far."

He was used to being waited on, Janie decided. A bit lazy too, perhaps. But he did have a nice sense of humor. You could tell that by the quirks at the corners of his mouth. His eyes were the color of sherry wine. Red hair meant a temper, perhaps, and the thrust of his chin was stubborn. That was all right. Janie had no respect for people who acted like door mats. He looked expensive—his shoes, his Panama hat, the golden-brown necktie knotted in a careless but knowing fashion . . .

"Well, what have you decided about me?" he asked with a crinkly smile.

Janie was conscious of the fact that she had been staring. A warm pink flush stained her cheeks.

"Tell me," he urged.

"Some time, maybe," she compromised. "When I've found out if I am right."

"Cautious?"

"Just trying to be polite . . . You'll stay for dinner, of course." Janie borrowed the voice that Mother used when she wanted to be especially gracious. "I'll speak to the cook."

"You weren't expecting me," he objected. "I'd better find a hotel."

"It will be all right." Janie fervently hoped that she was telling the truth. "We'll just set another place."

"Thank you." He settled back in the rocker.

"Excuse me for just a minute." Janie rose intending to make a graceful and dignified exit. The gum drops prevented that. Brushed by her skirt, the paper sack opened and sent them rattling down to the floor. Impossible to be dignified surrounded

by scurrying gum drops, tiny ones, pink and yellow
and green. If they had been bon-bons she wouldn't
have minded so much. But gum drops were child-
ish. Janie felt as though she had been caught stealing jam.

She looked up from the gum drops to Father's
young doctor. He was smiling. Not making fun,
she was grateful to him for that, but smiling the
way you would smile at a child you rather liked.
Janie smiled, too. Straight up into his startled eyes
she smiled her wide gay gorgeous smile that everyone said was lovely.

"Whew!" The exclamation was a long whistling
sound of surprise. "What happened? What did
that?"

"I smiled," Janie explained and felt foolish a
moment afterwards.

"Was that it?" His voice sounded bewildered.
"I thought somebody had turned on a moon. Do
you do it often?"

"Not very."

"You should." He looked at her as though he
hadn't seen her before. "It's a marvellous smile.
Why did you do it then?"

"I was thinking," Janie confessed, "that whenever I try to be dignified, I only succeed in acting
exactly like—Janie."

She knew he was watching her as she crossed to
open the door. She prayed that she wouldn't trip

over the sill. Her prayer was answered. She
didn't.

III

The kitchen of the old brick house was ruled by
a grumpy queen. No one was allowed to poach on
Rachel's private preserve. Rachel was a fat elderly
colored woman who had lived with the Ballard's
since Janie was a baby. She was devoted to all of
them though you would never have guessed it from
her grumpy complaining manner. Rachel was a
pearl beyond price but Rachel was also a tyrant.
You consulted her first on household matters that
had to do with parties or menus or guests.

When Janie entered the kitchen, Rachel was par-
ing potatoes. She sat, spreading out over the edges,
on a stool by the open back door. Her expression
was mournful and the song that she sang was a
dirge, a sure indication that Rachel was in fairly
good spirits and quite at peace with the world.

"What are we having for dinner?"

The dirge stopped short of a quavering note.
Rachel glanced up. The gold-brimmed spectacles,
which were the pride of her heart, gave her the look
of a plump and indignant brown owl.

"Hash," she answered briefly, "and het over
apple dumplin's."

"We're having company, Rachel." There was

real distress in Janie's voice. "We can't feed him hash and warmed over apple dumplings."

Rachel was not concerned. Janie explored the ice-box.

"Here's to-morrow's chicken," she called back over her shoulder. "You can fry it and make some tea cakes."

"What yo' maw gwine say if there's nothin' but bones fo' Sunday dinnah?" Rachel grumpily inquired.

"Mother won't care. Please, Rachel darling."

Rachel was as firm and unyielding as the ancient rock of Gibraltar.

"I ain't cookin' no fancy meal," she announced. "Dis here's mah lodge-meetin' night."

Janie resorted to trickery. There was one sure way of bringing Rachel to terms.

"All right," she said, "then I'll take him out to Aunt Rhoda's. Lily can get a nice dinner in less than no time at all."

Rachel pricked up her ears.

"Lemme tell you, Miss Janie," she said in impressive tones. "Lilly Summerses' tea cakes can't hold no candles to mine."

"I know that." Janie's voice was grave but her left eyebrow cocked itself drolly. "I just don't want to bother you because it's your lodge-meeting night. I'll take him out to Aunt Rhoda's."

"No sich thing!" Rachel heaved herself up from

the stool. "What yo' paw gwine say if you take comp'ny out beggin' for a meal?"

"Father," Janie said demurely, "always tells us never to bother you."

"You go set de table." Rachel lumbered over to the ice-box and lowered herself with a grunt. "Doctah Jawn's comp'ny ain't gwine resk his life wid Lily Summerses' tea cakes."

"You're a darling!" Janie embraced Rachel, the chicken and a bunch of asparagus with equal and ardent fervor. "Aunt Rhoda's Lily is not in your class at all."

"Go on wid you!" Rachel gave Janie a gentle shove. "How Ah'm gwine make any progress wid you clamped tight to mah neck? Jest you set de table pretty whilest Ah th'ow dis bird in de pan."

Before she set the table with Grandmother Ballard's silver and what was left of the rose-spray china, Janie did a curious thing. She walked into the living-room and took from the shelf of the old-fashioned square piano a photograph of Celia. It was a beautiful photograph, expensively framed in silver. Janie studied it thoughtfully. Celia was lovely. The light shining through her hair gave her an ethereal look. You thought of a Christmas-card angel. You thought of a porcelain saint in a silver niche . . .

For a moment she hesitated. Her hand moved to replace the photograph. She changed her mind.

With a small bronze ornament she shattered the glass in the silver frame. Then she carried it out into the hall closet, wrapped it in a raincoat and buried it under a pile of old galoshes. Janie was honest and hated deceit; but Janie was only human.

❧ II ❧

I

YOUNG DOCTOR KENNEDY, encumbered with an array of expensive luggage, followed Janie up a wide flight of polished stairs. The old brick house was deceiving on the outside, he thought, noticing with some surprise the Chesterfield in the hall, a fine oil painting, the grandfather's clock on the landing where the steps branched right and left. It was shabby, of course, but it had an air. You felt, even on so slight an acquaintance, that the Chesterfield and the painting and the clock had not been purchased in auction rooms and dubious antique shops. They had the appearance of having grown where they were placed, like trees in a friendly garden.

That, he reminded himself, was what Louise would term a quaint idea. His face in the clock-case mirror reflected a sheepish grin. Then it occurred to him that, for a year at least, Louise would not be around to label his ideas. He could be as quaint as he liked without feeling sheepish about

31

it. That, on the whole, was rather pleasant. He decided to begin by thinking that the banister rail would make a corking slide. The thought, he supposed, was the result of a suppressed desire. He had always wanted to slide down a banister rail.

"Mother would probably put you in the guest room." Janie led the way into a dim spacious room at the rear on the second floor. "I think this is nicer. Besides," she added, opening shutters and raising blinds, "you aren't exactly a guest."

"No." He dropped the luggage and flexed his aching arms. "I'm a legacy—like Mr. F.'s aunt."

"Oh!" Her face brightened with pleasure. "You've read 'Little Dorrit'!"

"Guilty," he said. "But please don't hold it against me."

"Do you like Dickens?"

Her voice indicated that this was, somehow, a very important matter.

"Is it a necessary qualification," he asked, "for living in Mulberry Square?"

"It helps," she gravely assured him. "If you think people are interesting—all sorts of people, I mean—you may even like the Square."

That possibility, he thought, at the present seemed rather remote. Still, this was a pleasant room. The long side-windows opened out on a balcony formed by the roof of the porch downstairs. Between them was a fireplace. The furni-

ture was of carved walnut, heavy but not oppressive
because the room was large and the ceiling was
high. The armchair beside the hearth was upholstered in material which had faded from red to
a dull raspberry shade. It matched the rug and
the window-hangings and the tufts on the candle-
wick spread. Over it all was a faint perfume.
Cedar, he thought, and lemon verbena and the locust
blossoms so close outside.

"It's strange, isn't it," he said, surveying his new
quarters with approval, "that some rooms seem to
welcome you and make you feel at home." That,
too, was a "quaint" idea. This small grave person
named Janie, however, did not seem to be preju-
diced against them. Again her face lighted swiftly
with pleasure.

"It is a nice room," she said. "You can see the
garden and the sunset."

He crossed to the rear window and looked out
over her head. The sunset promised to be satis-
factory, he thought. But it wasn't much of a garden, thinking in terms of Southampton and
Newport and Beverly Hills. For Mulberry
Square, however, it was probably an achievement to
have an arbor shading a flagstone walk, four apple
trees, peonies and mock-orange blossoms, hollyhocks
marching in gaudy files along the high brick walls.
There was a catalpa tree girdled with a circular
wooden seat and a summer house tangled with vines.

At the end of the arbor a gate opened into the alleyway beyond and morning glories scrambled over a building which once had been a stable, no doubt, and now was a double garage.

It certainly needed attention. The roses mingled sociably with the poppies and nasturtiums. The arbor sagged under its weight of vines. The bird-bath was tilted and rimmed with moss. But it had an air. You felt that children had played on the grass and swung from the apple tree boughs. You felt—Good Lord! Young Doctor Kennedy reined in his flying fancies with a return of the sheepish grin. But there was something about it, something he had missed . . .

"It's a very nice garden," he said.

"It used to be." Janie sighed for vanished glories. "No one has time any more. There's only Rachel and Stoney . . . Oh, there's old Thomas coming in at the gate!"

Young Doctor Kennedy watched a burley old man walking up under the arbor towards the house.

"Is 'Thomas' a friend of yours?" he asked thinking that the rugged old chap looked a little like the gardener at Roselyn.

"My oldest friend," Janie explained. "He used to be the caretaker of the Square. They lived on Juniper street when I was a little girl but now that his grandson Tom is a lawyer, they've moved right up in the Square. He's Scotch and plays the bagpipes and has a wonderful garden. If you'll excuse me, I'll go down and see what he's brought."

Young Doctor Kennedy remained at the window. He smiled at the sound of her footsteps hurrying down the stairs. Presently he saw her running across the grass to meet the burly old man.

"Hello, Thomas." Her voice was charming, young Doctor Kennedy thought, low and a bit husky, sprinkled with gay little laughing notes.

"I brought you a bit of a present." A gruff voice thickened with a Scottish burr.

"Strawberries!" An excited squeal. "They're lovely, Thomas."

"Mary thought you had company, Miss Janie."

"It's Father's young doctor. He came this afternoon."

The red-haired young man retreated behind the window-hanging. What was that about eaves-droppers? But he needn't have worried. Janie's interest, just then, was centered in the basket.

"They're lovely and red. I do hate green berries, don't you? You're a darling, Thomas, and also a precious lamb!"

Young Doctor Kennedy, watching behind the window-hanging, was surprised to see her set the basket on the grass and throw both arms around the burly old Scotchman's neck.

"Well," he thought, when he had recovered sufficiently to think at all, "that was a 'quaint' idea!"

II

The rear window interfered rather seriously with
young Doctor Kennedy's unpacking. He found
himself drawn there frequently, attracted by voices
in the garden. Already he had identified certain
members of the family. The fat colored woman
was Rachel, of course. The charcoal giant, turning
an ice-cream freezer in the shade of the catalpa
tree was Stoney—Stonewall Jackson, perhaps.
Stoney was a figure to intrigue the imagination. He
looked like a pugilist. His face was battered and
criss-crossed with scars. The muscles bulged under
his cotton shirt; his chest and shoulders were enormous. But for all his apparent strength, Hugh observed that the freezer whirred more briskly
whenever Rachel bulked into sight. Rachel, he had
decided, was the officer in command.

"Mother" was the pretty plump little woman in
the flowered dress. She must, he thought, be very
much younger than Doctor Ballard. She had hurried out to speak to the charcoal giant with the
curious scars on his face. Her manner seemed a
bit flurried. He hoped that his unexpected arrival
was not upsetting things. A call of "Mother"
had sent her hurrying back into the house. That
was Janie's voice, "Mother! Tom McAllister has
sent Celia lilies-of-the-valley! Isn't that the luck-
iest thing!"

Celia! Young Doctor Kennedy wondered about
her as he turned into chaos the order among his
luggage achieved that morning by his brother-in-
law's valet. Celia and lilies-of-the-valley. Who
was Celia? A sister, perhaps. Celia and lilies-of-
the-valley. They went together, somehow. Both
were cool and fragrant. Voices in the garden.
Perhaps Celia was there. He returned to the window
half expecting to see a cool and and lovely maiden
with lilies-of-the-valley bunched in her slender white
hands.

He was disappointed. Janie was talking to a
stout middle-aged woman with grayish hair strained
back from a round red face and a billowy bosom
encased in snuff-colored gingham.

"Angel cake!" Gay little laughing notes sprinkling themselves through the air. "Oh, thank you,
Mrs. Quillen!"

"It's a pleasure, darlin'," A bluff hearty voice
well flavored with brogue.

"It looks almost too good to eat."

"Go on wid your blarney! Mary seen a taxi
stop an' a somebody git out wid luggage. It's the
Divvil himsilf as send comp'ny when there isn't a
scrap of cake in the house."

"Thank you a hundred times. What a perfectly
beautiful plate!"

"Ain't it now?" A degree of complacency in the
bluff hearty voice. "Mary got it wid tradin' stamps.
The best ain't none too good for a saint on earth

like your father. There ain't no hurry. You can
keep it as long as you want."

The snuff-colored bosom became a snuff-colored
back moving ponderously under the arbor and out
at the alley-way gate.

"Mother!" Another excited squeal. "Mrs.
Quillen just brought us an angel cake."

"So I see." "Mother's" voice with a bit of an
edge. "I wish they wouldn't keep running in here."

"Mother!" The gay little laughing notes
drowned in a flood of reproach. "She only meant
to be kind."

"Of course, dear." A soothing tone suggesting
patience with the whims of a difficult child. "But
you needn't be quite so *intimate*."

The lady of the manor! Mother, apparently,
drew lines. It was a good thing, Hugh thought
with a chuckle of amusement, that she hadn't seen
Janie embracing the burly old Scotchman.

He moved around the room, hanging things in
the wardrobe, opening bureau drawers. Gradually
the chaos was restored to order again. At the bot-
tom of a calf-skin case lay his evening clothes. He
lifted them out with a rueful sort of expression.
Wouldn't need them here, he supposed. A wisp of
pink chiffon fluffed out of one of the pockets.
Madge Copeland's handkerchief! He permitted
himself a moment or two of regret. Not for
Madge, exactly, but for the easy, gay life he had
left behind. He wouldn't be swimming this summer

with Louise and Rod and the Temple girls. Madge
wouldn't be tucking her handkerchief into his pocket
between dances at the club. Oh, well . . .

A shriek in the garden. Young Doctor Kennedy
returned again to the window. A small white dog
was streaking across the grass with Janie in hot
pursuit. The garden was thrown into sudden confusion. Stoney left the ice-cream freezer, calling:
"Here dog." "Nice li'l Tweedles!" in a voice as
mild as the bleat of a lamb. Mother, panting a
little, joined the chase. Rachel lumbered down the
back porch steps with a pink-lined willow basket.

From the din and fuss, young Doctor Kennedy
judged that the small white dog was a cherished
family treasure. He was surprised, accordingly,
to hear Janie exclaim as she yanked him out of the
poppy-bed, "You nasty mean little thing!"

"Thank goodness!" Mother was holding her
hand against her side. "Celia would never have
forgiven us."

"Rats!" Janie dumped the small white dog into
the willow basket. "She wouldn't care if he hung
himself on the gate."

"Janie!" A somewhat breathless reproach.
"Celia is always kind to her pets."

"She let the Persian cat Bob gave her starve,"
said Janie. "And the love birds that old widower
sent her froze to death because ——"

"Janie!" Just for a moment young Doctor Kennedy thought that "Mother" had glanced up at the

window. He was glad that the hanging concealed him. It wasn't polite to spy on family scenes. "That isn't kind," "Mother" continued sweetly. "Celia is devoted to Tweedles."

"Well she won't be now." Janie was marching herself towards the house. "Ned Ferris, you know, is engaged to somebody else."

Celia, the red-haired young man at the window reflected, was evidently a belle. He wondered about the scene in the garden for a moment and then put it out of his mind. But Celia was not to be so lightly dismissed. Ten minutes later, as he brushed his hair with vigorous strokes, he found himself singing in an unremarkable barytone:

> *Who is Celia? What is she,*
> *That all the swains adore her?*

III

"I'm glad to see you, my boy."

Doctor Ballard, tall, white haired, a little stooped, stood at the foot of the stairs with Janie clinging like a green cocoon to his arm. Young Doctor Kennedy was embarrassed, for the moment, by a choked feeling in his throat. No one had called him "my boy" in that fatherly way since he was sixteen years old . . . "My boy" . . . He swallowed twice.

"Thank you, sir."

"I'm sorry about your letter." The doctor was

holding his hand in a warm friendly clasp. "It's a failing of mine." His eyes twinkled. "How about that, Janie?"

"I told him Father. I explained how you are about letters."

"That's all right."

"I can keep you busy, I promise you that." Young Doctor Kennedy thought he never had seen such a kindly, heart-warming smile. "We'll try our best to make you happy as well."

"Thank you, sir."

A gong sounded four ringing notes.

"Supper, youngsters. Come on."

They walked together out into the dining-room, Doctor Ballard in the middle, one arm around Janie and the other arm around Hugh. "Mother," very flushed and pretty in her flowered dress met them at the door.

"How do you do, Doctor Kennedy." She smiled and gave him her hand.

"Call him Hugh. How about it, my boy?"

"My boy" . . . Damn that choke in his throat.

"I'd like it much better, Mrs. Ballard."

"Hugh then, of course . . . I'm afraid you'll just have to take pot-luck. If we had known you were coming——"

"Now, Helen——" Doctor Ballard embraced them all in the genial warmth of his smile. "Don't try to make him feel like a guest. Hugh has just come home."

❧ III ❧

I

THE Square was pleasant at night. Shadows concealed the ugly places. The houses with their jutting eaves had a certain old-fashioned charm. They were built of brick and similar in construction, six on two opposite sides of the Square, separated from each other by narrow brick court-yards and walls tangled over with vines. The front steps of each led up directly from the sidewalk but the fragrance of flowers, borne by the gentle wind, indicated that there were gardens at the rear. Touched with the magic of moonlight, the Square seemed to regain a little of its former dignity. You could forget that in the sunshine it was old and dingy and down at the heel.

"It's nicer at night, isn't it?" Janie asked a bit anxiously as she walked with Hugh beneath the flowering locusts. She wanted him to find the Square endurable, at least. Mother, at supper, had been so discouraging about it all.

"Much nicer," he agreed.

Janie thought that the words lacked enthusiasm.

"You're being polite," she said with a sigh. The sigh was prompted by sympathy. Janie, at that particular moment, was feeling sorry for Father's young doctor, sentenced to a year in the Square whether he liked it or not. "You think it's pretty dreadful."

"I did this afternoon," he confessed. "I had expected something rather different. My father used to tell me about it. I was—well, disappointed, to say the least."

"I know how you felt."

"How?" He smiled down at the small grave person marching along at his side. Friendly little thing . . .

"Like Rip Van Winkle," she answered, "when he returned to the village after his nap on the mountain. You thought that someone was playing tricks."

"Exactly." His ringing laugh caused some comment along the doorsteps.

"And you said to yourself, or maybe out loud, 'Must I live for a year in this God-forsaken place?' "

"The word was a bit stronger," he admitted. "And if I remember correctly it was addressed to the ladies on the fountain."

"They couldn't hear you," she gravely assured him. "There's only one ear for the three."

"I'll apologize anyway." He bowed in the direction of the fountain. "They look rather lovely to-night."

Everything looked different, he thought, in the silver wash of moonlight. This afternoon it had seemed hopelessly forlorn. The houses must have been charming once with their balconies and court-yards, their walled gardens and grilled iron gates. The fan-lights were interesting. They might have been suggested by a pigeon's outspread tail, the great-great-grandfather of the pigeons that cooed tonight in the eaves.

He was finding it pleasant to walk with this friendly small person beneath the shadowy locusts. Her comments amused him, her whole-hearted in-terest in the lives of these commonplace people; the burly old Scotchman smoking his pipe in a door-way, the angel-cake woman boxing a small boy's ears, the twins in a clothes-basket chariot drawn by a thin little girl. She was evidently a favorite in the Square. Their leisurely stroll was frequently interrupted.

"Hello, Nina." A handsome girl leaning half out of a window. Dusky hair, enormous dark eyes, a sullen red underlip.

"Hello, Janie." A golden voice with the quality of a 'cello.

"This is Father's young doctor."

"How do you do." Enormous black eyes turn-ing at once to Janie. "If you see my kids, send them home."

"That's Nina Mantel," Janie explained when they had left the dusky beauty behind.

"Her children? She seems rather young."

"They're her brothers. But Nina has raised them, I guess. The mother deserted them years ago. Professor Mantel gives violin lessons. Nina has a beautiful voice."

"I noticed that."

"Father says she might be famous if she could have it trained. But she has to wash those boys and feed them and mend their clothes."

They walked on to the house next door.

"Good-evening, Miss Ellie." A thin little woman in gray scurrying down the steps.

"Oh, it's you, Janie." A frightened expression. A hat with one pink rose.

"This is Father's young doctor."

"Good-evening." A bow and a murmur. Fidgeting fingers in cotton gloves. Shabby kid slippers poised for flight.

"How is your mother, Miss Ellie?"

"No better, I'm afraid. If you'll excuse me ——" A nervous cough. "I—I have an errand."

She slipped past them like a small gray ghost, crossed the street and was swallowed up by the shadows.

"She's gone to meet her beau." Janie's voice was warm with sympathy. "You can tell by the rose in her hat."

"Why doesn't he come here to see her?"

"He sells dress-goods in Leland's department store. Old Mrs. Pope is a Lucas."

"Royal purple?"

"Something like that. Miss Ellie does dress-making." She indicated a modest sign in the window. "Old Mrs. Pope lives upstairs. She simply ignores the dressmaking and pretends the house hasn't any downstairs at all."

"Funny!"

"I think it's pathetic."

"You, I mean."

"Oh!" . . .

An interval of silence. Silver-edged shadows falling across the sidewalk. Children playing "Hide and Seek," their voices piping and shrill. Girls in petal-colored frocks and boys in their Sunday best . . . "Hello, Janie." "Hello, Agnes. Hello, Jim." . . . Women with baskets coming home from up-town . . . "It's awful, the price of eggs." "Three for a quarter at the A.&P." . . . Men in groups discussing the news of the day . . . "The A's won again." "Paid Fire Department." "Do away with the volunteers." . . . A woman calling from an upstairs window . . . "Johnny! Margaret! Come in here! It's almost nine o'clock!" The hurdy-gurdy by the fountain . . . "We strolled the lanes together" . . . The Square on Saturday night . . .

"Hello, Uncle Charlie." A round rosy old man at the gate in the corner wall. Old King Cole in pearl gray trousers and an ancient swallow-tailed coat.

"Well, Janie. How's the authoress to-night?"

"Fine. But you look bothered."

"Rhoda sent a woman to clean. She's been at it all day and not through yet. Damned nuisance! I wish I was asleep."

"This is Father's young doctor."

"Owen Kennedy's son!" A waggish smile. The clasp of a puffy old hand. "I'm glad to see you, my boy."

"Mistah Cha'lie!" A kinky gray head popped out of a downstairs window. An old negro, the arc-light full in his face.

"What is it, Jeff?"

"Dis here cleanin' lady done axe fo' a flo' mop, suh."

"Tell her ——" A dismal groan. "Never mind, I'll see to it, Jeff. Come calling, Janie, and bring Owen Kennedy's son. Floor mops! My sainted Aunt Maria! I wish I was asleep!"

Great-uncle Charlie bounced into the house, his swallow-tails flying behind.

"He's a darling." Gay little notes laughing in Janie's voice. "But he hates to be house-cleaned, poor dear. He lives here alone with Jeff. When he's bothered, he wishes he was asleep."

"Look here, young lady."

Janie glanced up swiftly. The arc-light shone on her soft brown hair and her little pointed face.

"What is it, please?"

"I have a name you know."

"But it wouldn't mean anything to them."

"Will I always be 'Father's Young Doctor'?"

"Perhaps . . . Unless they like you enough to give you a name of your own."

That was something to think about. But he didn't do it just then. They had crossed the street and were walking along a grilled iron fence, higher than either of their heads. Behind it were lawns, a thicket of shrubbery, a house with fluted white pillars.

"That's a fine old place."

"The Governor's House. Uncle Frank Grove owns it now. Aunt Lucy lived here with Muriel and John."

"The Governor's House?"

"A governor lived here years ago. They've called it that ever since. It used to be lovely. Aunt Lucy moved away when the mills came so close. They have a summer home outside town. In the winter they live in Washington. This place has been vacant for nearly ten years."

Janie thought sadly of the Governor's House as it used to be. Hugh thought, with a curious sort of resentment, of the Governor's House as it was. They approached the entrance.

"Hello, Tom." A thick-set young man of medium height locking the gate in the grilled iron fence.

"Hello, Janie." A pleasant voice, crisp and decisive.

"They haven't sold it, have they, Tom?"

"I don't think so. The kids have been sneaking in. I wanted to see if they've done any damage."

"Oh!" Janie was obviously relieved. "This is —Doctor Kennedy, Mr. McAllister."

"Glad to know you." The grip of a muscular hand.

"He's going to work with Father for a year."

"Good."

Hugh felt himself being closely inspected. He returned the compliment. Strong features, he thought. Eyes with a dreamy expression which, somehow, seemed out of place. Thirty-two or three, perhaps. Well tailored and barbered and groomed. But why that measuring look?

"Is Celia at home?" Again the crisp decisive voice.

"She's at the shore with Aunt Rose." A rather stiff sort of answer. Didn't she like the chap?

"I didn't know . . . Well, good-night. I'll probably see you again."

He lifted his hat and walked away, authority in his swinging stride; a confident, self-assured air.

"That's old Thomas' grandson Tom," Janie confided in the way that made them comrades standing shoulder to shoulder against a hostile world. "He worked his way through college and law school and now he's very successful. Father says he'll probably be the next burgess."

"Looks rather young."

"He's brilliant." Evidently, Hugh thought, she

didn't dislike the chap. She was chanting praises
to the burly old Scotchman's grandson Tom. "People like him—especially in this part of town. He
lives here with old Thomas when he might have
moved out on Manor street or the Heights. They
like that, Father says. He used to mow the lawn
for Uncle Frank and drive Aunt Lucy to market.
Gracious!" Janie interrupted herself with a low
throaty sound of amusement. "Many's the time
he's fished me out of the fountain and spanked me
and sent me home."

Hugh wondered about that measuring look as
they walked on along the high grilled fence.

"Celia?" he asked, out of a thoughtful silence.

"My sister . . . That's a magnolia tree up there
close to the house."

II

It was quiet under the mulberry trees. The
hurdy-gurdy had trundled itself away. The children, too, were gone and the shabby old men who
sat at night in the Square. Only the nymphs were
left, silver-spangled, dancing with arms upflung.

They sat on a bench near the fountain with the
mulberry leaves, rough and heart-shaped and silver-
lined, stirring above their heads. The sounds of
the town came to them faintly; the rattle of a
trolley, a pounding truck, a car changing gears on
the upgrade of Orange street. All about them were

shadows and the heavy sweet fragrance of the locust blossoms. Janie sighed blissfully.

"Sometimes," she said, "I love this funny old Square."

"Only sometimes?" Hugh glanced down at Janie seated with one foot tucked under on the rusty iron bench. She looked, he thought, like a solemn brownie strayed in from a forest somewhere. Quaint little thing. He rejected the word. That was Louise's label for delicate whimsical things. She shouldn't label, if he could help it, this friendly amusing child. "Only sometimes?" he repeated.

"Well," she confessed, "sometimes I hate it, of course."

"Why do you like it to-night?"

Janie was quite unable to formulate an answer. She didn't know why. She knew only that she felt like golden bubbles inside. You couldn't explain why you were happy. That was like pulling off butterfly wings. You just felt it; a lump in your throat, a singing somewhere in your heart.

"I don't know." She wished she could take out her emotions and dress them in pretty words. Celia could. Janie couldn't. People thought, because of that, she didn't feel things at all. But Father knew. She had heard him say once to Mother, "Celia can take care of herself. But I worry sometimes about Janie. She cares so terribly." Mother had laughed and said, "Why John, that's absurd. Janie hardly ever cries." . . . "I don't know," she repeated.

"Of course you don't," he said gently. "It's a mixture of all sorts of things."

Janie's face brightened with her swift lighted look of pleasure. Miraculously, this red-haired young man seemed to understand. She looked up at him gratefully from under her shadowy lashes. He wasn't smiling his crinkly smile; his eyes were thoughtful and almost sad. Suddenly she wanted to know all about him; what kind of a little boy he had been, where he had lived and gone to school.

"Tell me about you," she said.

"It would make a dull story." He was smiling again. "There aren't any thrilling adventures."

"I don't care. Tell me anyway." She folded her hands in her lap.

"Well," he began, "once upon a time ——"

"I'm not exactly a baby."

"Of course you aren't." His manner was deeply apologetic. "I seem to keep forgetting."

"As long as that's understood, you can tell it any way you like. Really, you know," she admitted, "I like stories that begin 'Once upon a time.'"

"So do I. You can fib a bit. Nobody expects them to be true." He paused to light a cigarette and then began again. "Once upon a time there was a red-haired little boy . . ."

Janie, listening intently, travelled back with him

to the brownstone house in New York. His mother, she learned, was dead. His sister and his brother were ten and twelve years older than he.

". . . So this little boy was pretty lonesome sometimes. He would go through a glass tunnel filled with plants ——"

"A conservatory?" Janie was becoming more and more impressed.

"This little boy named Hugh called it a glass tunnel with green things growing up through the floor. At the end of the tunnel was a door and behind the door was his father's office. Sometimes, if there weren't any ladies in white kid gloves having their nerves repaired, his father would tell him about a place called Mulberry Square where everybody was friendly and had a lovely time."

"That's strange, isn't it?" Janie marveled, "your knowing about us so long ago."

"The audience will please not interrupt." Hugh blew a smoke ring that was almost perfect.

"I won't again."

"Promise?"

"Cross my heart."

". . . And then . . ."

Tragedy stalked into the story. His brother had been killed in an automobile accident. He hurried over that part. His sister Louise had married. She was Mrs. Roderick Payson VanHorn. Janie thought that was a very elegant name.

". . . So this little boy, only he was larger now
and his voice croaked like a bull-frog's, went away
to school. He wore a uniform and learned to ride
a horse and shoot at things . . ."

Janie pictured him in a uniform, very stiff and
erect, with his chest thrust out and his eyes staring
straight ahead. She wished she had known him
then. But Father said he was twenty-six. Gracious! She'd have been only ten or eleven. He
wouldn't have noticed her then.

". . . One day—" he paused and his eyes again
were sad. "Well, anyway, there wasn't anyone left
in the brownstone house with the tunnel . . ."

His father had died! Janie, sympathizing, felt
tears on her lashes.

". . . So Hugh went to college. When he was
twenty-one, a man with a nut-cracker face told him
that sometime he would have to go to Mulberry
Square. But he didn't mind. His father had told
him everybody had a lovely time."

"It's changed so," Janie mourned, "since your
father used to come for visits with Father."

"The audience will probably get warts," Hugh
prophesied darkly. "She crossed her heart and
broke a promise."

"I'm sorry."

"That doesn't cure warts . . . Hugh," he continued, "who was, by this time rather a handsome
young man, finished college and went to medical

school. He worked pretty hard and played sometimes and fell in and out of love . . ."

He spent vacations with his sister, Janie learned.
Newport, Bar Harbor, Murray Bay. You read
about places like that in the picture sections of the
Sunday papers . . . "Doctor Hugh Kennedy, of
New York," snapped on the beach at Newport with
Miss Genevieve So-and-So, wealthy Chicago heiress.
. . . Heavens! How could he be expected to live
in Mulberry Square!

". . . So he went into a hospital and wore a
white uniform and grew a mustache and shaved it
off because it turned out to be red . . ."

Janie tried to imagine him with a mustache. The
attempt was unsuccessful. She abandoned it at once.

". . . And then, one day, he came to Mulberry
Square. That same evening, he sat on a bench and
told a story to a little girl named Janie with hazel
eyes and a pointed chin and a perfectly gorgeous
smile. And that," he finished, "is all."

"But why?" Janie asked when she had thanked
him for the story, "did your father want you to
come?"

"I rather suspect," he answered, "that the 'Lorelei' is to blame."

The "Lorelei"! . . . *"Ich weiss nicht was soll es
bedeuten"* . . . Janie saw her, a languorous blonde
with slanting green eyes. But, of course, she might
be mistaken.

"What does she look like?" she asked.

"She's white all over with graceful lines and trimmings of solid brass."

What a strange description! Janie looked up to see if he was teasing. His face, she observed, was grave but twinkles frisked in his eyes.

"And," he added, amused at her bewildered expression, "she wears a striped sunbonnet over her after-deck."

"Oh!" Janie at once was immensely relieved. "It's a boat!"

"The Lorelei," he insisted. "She lures young doctors away from their stethoscopes and makes them idle and useless."

Janie understood.

"You won't have a chance to be worthless here," she gravely assured him. "We row when we go on the river. There isn't a single Lorelei in all of Mulberry Square."

III

The town clock struck eleven. They walked slowly through the Square and across to the opposite side. Everything was quiet now. They passed the church on the corner and the small stone rectory almost smothered in vines. A messenger boy was clicking the rectory gate.

"Hello, Johnny Quillen."

"Hi, Janie."

"There are a great many 'Johns' around here," Hugh remarked.

"That's because it's Father's name."

"Are they all named for him?"

"Everybody loves Father." Janie was bursting with pride. It showed in her eyes and in the tilt of her chin. "He's always doing things for people. There's Stoney, for instance."

"The young giant who drove my car into the garage?"

Janie nodded.

"Father found him one night down in Shanty-town all cut to pieces after a fight. He patched him up and brought him home. I think Stoney would die for Father."

"He's splendid."

"You'll see," Janie said softly, "when you've been here a little while."

The Ballards' wall began at the end of the rectory fence. They passed the gate which led to the side veranda and walked on to the entrance. The twin iron lanterns were shining on either side of the arched white doorway. The fan-light made a yellow design on the sidewalk beyond the steps.

"It's old, isn't it?" Hugh was looking up at the tracery of vines against the mellow brick walls.

"I'll show you something." Janie tugged at his arm.

Wondering a little, he followed her to the office

entrance at the corner. On the wall beside the
grilled gate with its twin twinkling lanterns was a
brass plate engraved with the name of Doctor John
Curtis Ballard.

"This," Janie ran a forefinger over the letters,
"is more than a hundred years old."

"But your father ———"

"My grand-father was Doctor John Ballard and
so was his father, too."

"Oh!"

The office door opened. A young woman with
a child in her arms walked down the shallow steps.
Doctor Ballard, tall, white haired, a little stooped,
stood in the open doorway.

"Do as I told you, Martha. Use the lotion three
times a day."

"I'll try." A weary young voice. "But you
know how it is with us. Sam hasn't worked
for ———"

"Get it at Smith's and have it charged to me."

"Oh, thank you, Doctor!"

The door closed. The woman, lifting her shoulders, opened the gate.

"Good-evening, Martha."

"Hello, Janie."

"Is the baby sick?"

"A rash. He's covered all over . . . Janie Ballard, your father is the kindest man who ever lived."

"See?" Janie glanced up at Hugh.

He squeezed her hand.

"Yes Janie," he said.   "I see."

IV

Janie said her prayers that night.   She knelt in the dark beside her narrow white bed.   The petition followed a familiar formula.   There was only one deviation.   "Make Aunt Rose better," she said half aloud.   "But, please God, not too soon."

⚜ IV ⚜

I

THE Square did not accept Hugh all at once.
It was inclined to regard with suspicion this
unfamiliar young doctor. He had a way of losing
his temper and speaking unpleasant truths. There
was the case of old Mrs. Pope.

"She says I'm not to come back again," Hugh
announced one afternoon.

"Who?" Doctor Ballard, seated on the shady
side porch, looked up from a medical journal.

"That old harridan, Mrs. Pope." Hugh's face
wore an expression of indignation and injured pride
which caused Doctor Ballard to smile.

"What did she say?" he asked.

"She said she wouldn't be insulted by a red-
haired young whipper-snapper who had no respect
for age," Hugh faithfully reported.

"You'll have to dye your hair, I suppose." The
Doctor's eyes were twinkling. "Did you insult her,
Hugh?"

"I told her there was nothing the matter with

her heart and it wouldn't kill her to walk down-stairs."

"Serves her right." Doctor Ballard laughed. "But," he added more gravely, "as much as they need it, you can't go around lighting firecrackers under people. You're new to them and young and ——"

"Conceited?" Hugh was smiling, too.

"Intolerant was the word I meant. Win their confidence, my boy. Then you can insult them as much as you like."

Hugh attempted to follow the Doctor's advice. He seemed, in those first bewildering weeks, to make no progress at all. Janie noted the passing events with anxious and critical eyes. No mother bird watching her fledgling's first attempt to use his wings could have been more concerned.

"I think I know what's the matter," she said as they sat on the side porch one evening after office hours which had been particularly trying.

"What?" Hugh snapped the question.

"Well you might at least be polite." Janie moved away from him into the far corner of the hammock.

"I'm sorry." He reached for her hand. "Come back, young fellow. I really want to know."

Janie accepted the apology and the invitation.

"You're too ——" She searched for the appro-priate word. "You're too formal, Hugh."

"Formal?"

"I mean you're not friendly enough. Now to-night, for instance, when the General was in the office ——"

"You mean that old soak with the wooden leg?" Janie interrupted her lecture to explain.

"Everybody calls him the General. He lives in that white-washed house over the railroad tracks and —— Well, anyway, Hugh, you just sat there like the Great Jehovah on a throne and fired long words at him all the time he was trying to tell you about the time he was shot in the Spanish-American War and ——"

"That didn't have anything to do with a carbuncle on his neck. Good Lord ——"

"But he wanted to tell you." Janie was very much in earnest. "Don't you see, Hugh, it probably made him feel brave to remember when he was a soldier. He was blowing himself a bugle and you didn't pay attention."

"You're a funny kid." Hugh was silent for a moment. "How did you know about it?"

"I peeped," she confessed. "In at the back office door."

"You did!" He laughed and squeezed her hand.

"Really, Hugh," she said gravely, "I think you'll probably be a grand doctor in about ten years. Now let's go see if there was any cake left from supper. Being an inspiration always makes me hungry."

Hugh made an honest effort to be friendly. He had no trouble with the uptown patients. Manor

street and the sacred Heights were willing to give
him a chance.   Doctor Ballard's practise, however,
was largely confined to the mill district surrounding the Square and the criss-crossed alleys of
Shantytown beyond the railroad tracks.   There
Hugh felt himself to be openly resented and se-
cretly ridiculed.   Janie suggested a reason and a
remedy.

"It's this car," she said as they were riding home
from the playground one afternoon.

"What's the matter with it?"   Hugh was tired
and warm and exasperated.   At that particular moment, he hated Mulberry Square and the mill district and the hop-scotch alleys of Shantytown.

"It's too gorgeous."

"Good Lord!   What ——"

"Don't you see, Hugh?"   Janie's small flushed
face, smudgy with dust, was very grave.   "If you
ride in a car like this, they think you couldn't possibly understand their troubles.   It's like when Aunt
Lucy drives down to take them baskets at Christmas
time in her mink coat and —— I mean, well, most
of the time it's a friend they want and not a doctor
at all."

"Shall I rig myself up like St. Francis and walk
through Shantytown with pigeons perched on my
shoulders?"

"Silly!   Of course not.   But you needn't be quite
so—so magnificent.   See?"

"I'm damned if I do."   Hugh brought the car
to a stand-still with a vicious slurring of brakes.

"You have a terrible temper."   Janie dismounted
from the long maroon-colored roadster with her
chin in the air.   "I don't see how we stand you!"

She didn't expect him to take her advice.   She
was surprised when he came for her the following
afternoon in a second-hand roadster very much the
worse for wear.

"Is this bad enough?" he asked with a sheepish
grin.   "We could tear off the fenders and give it a
couple of kicks."

"It looks sort of friendly, I think."

"Hop in."   Hugh flung open the door.   "We'll
see how fast she can travel."

They named the car "Horatius."

"But why 'Horatius'?"   Doctor Ballard asked
when he was invited out in front of the house for
an after-supper inspection.

"Well, you see, Father," Janie made haste to explain, "it stalled on the White Marsh bridge and
Hugh couldn't start it and the cars coming the other
way couldn't pass.   There must have been twenty,
I guess, before we moved, all honking their horns
and racing their engines.   So we decided we'd name
it 'Horatius'."

Doctor Ballard laughed.   Mother looked puzzled.

"I don't see the connection," she said.

"Mother isn't acquainted with Mr. Macaulay."

Doctor Ballard smiled at Janie and Hugh as though they shared an amusing secret. "They didn't read such gory literature as 'The Lays of Ancient Rome' in Miss Parker's conservatory for female rose-buds."

Janie quoted rather freely:

> *"Then up spake brave Horatius*
> *A valiant man was he,*
> *Now, who will stand on either hand*
> *And guard the bridge with me?"*

Mother was not greatly enlightened.

"You aren't going to use that wreck, are you, Hugh?" she asked in a tone of distress.

"Never mind, Helen." The Doctor's eyes were twinkling. "Whenever you expect callers from Manor street, just tell Stoney. He'll run out Hugh's Packard and let it stand in front of the house."

"Use it if you like, Mrs. Ballard."

"Thank you, Hugh." Mother's expression changed. She pictured herself riding in state to call on the Manor street ladies. Too bad it wasn't a cabriolet. But Stoney could raise the top . . .

Whether or not the humble appearance of Horatius had anything to do with the gradual change from resentment to acceptance, Hugh was never able to decide. The Miller twin, however, certainly did. Hugh rushed into the Miller kitchen one after-noon to find the child purple and pop-eyed, ap-parently choking to death. Without waiting to ask questions, Hugh seized the little fellow, up-ended him and shook him vigorously. A piece of hard candy rolled down to the floor. Two minutes later the child, turned right side up, was sobbing quietly in his mother's arms.

This exhibition of medical skill could not have occurred in a more auspicious place. Mrs. Miller, the elder, was a tireless bearer of news. Before night all the Square, and a considerable portion of the surrounding territory, had been informed that "the young doctor" had saved the Miller twin's life. Mrs. Miller, the elder, seizing upon an excuse for dramatic recounting, had not spared lavish details. Hugh was the hero of the day. Even old Mrs. Pope, who had heard the news in some strange round-about way, observed to her daughter that she was glad the whipper-snapper was good for something besides insulting his elders.

"It wasn't anything," Hugh protested to Janie. "Common-sense. The mother would have thought of it herself if she hadn't been frightened out of her wits."

"You're a hero in spite of yourself." Janie favored with a glimpse of her wide gay smile. "It will make a difference. You wait and see."

It did make a difference. Hugh recognized the change in the atmosphere. It pleased him to a surprising degree. He wondered very often why he cared whether they liked him or not. He would be here only for a year. This was merely an interlude. It had nothing to do with his future failure or success.

But he did care. Pride, he supposed, and his admiration for Doctor Ballard. Then, too, there was Janie.

"I'm living up to you," he said one evening when she told him that Father was proud of the way he was getting on.

"Me?" Her eyes opened wide.

"You stick pretty close to that playground." His voice was teasing and tender, too. "It isn't a picnic in weather like this."

"Sometimes I hate it," Janie confessed. "But I'd be ashamed to quit."

"That's what I like about you, Janie." Hugh lazily swayed the hammock. "You're the most downright and honest young person I know."

Honest! Janie was stricken with remorse. She thought of Celia's photograph waiting to be called for at the gift-shop uptown. Honest! She felt a guilty flush creeping up to her forehead and down to her Peter Pan collar. She blessed the concealing shadows and made a stern resolve.

The next afternoon she left the playground early. When she reached home, after the walk uptown and back, she went directly into the living-room. Presently, Celia's photograph, the glass restored and the silver shining, stood on the shelf of the old-fashioned square piano. Beneath it Janie arranged lilies-of-the-valley in a low crystal bowl. She

thought of burning candles. They would be appro-
priate, she thought, since this was a sort of pen-
ance. She compromised by tilting the shade on the
piano lamp so that, at a touch of the button, it would
illuminate the shrine. Janie was grasping the nettle
in her own whole-hearted fashion.

After supper, she led Hugh into the living-room.
He was provokingly slow about noticing the photograph. He wandered aimlessly around the room
until Janie wanted to scream. At last, in despera-
tion, she seated herself on the piano bench and struck
a few wrong notes.

"Is this the tune," she asked, knowing very well
that it wasn't, "of the song you were playing last
night?"

"Lord no! Do you call that a tune?"

He was walking toward the piano. Janie felt an
impulse to dash Celia to the floor. She didn't, of
course. She moved over on the bench to make
room for Hugh. He seated himself beside her and
looked at the keys.

"Here you go." His fingers were picking out the
gay little sparkling tune . . .

> *Five feet tall*
> *Rather small*
> *That's my baby.*

Sure, now, that he was right, his eyes lifted from
the keys.

"Who's that?" His fingers continued, not very skillfully, to pick out the gay little tune.

"Celia."

"Oh . . ."

> *Curly hair*
> *Blue-eyed stare*
> *That's my baby.*

"Isn't she pretty?" Janie was grasping the nettle again.

"Gorgeous . . ." He struck a discord, frowned, found the right notes and, smiling down at Janie with a teasing twinkle in his ruddy brown eyes, he began all over again . . .

> *Five feet all*
> *Rather small*
> *That's my baby.*

II

"Janie, dear."

"Yes, Mother." Janie, lying on the grass under the catalpa tree, looked up from a magazine.

"If I were you ——" Mother paused. Janie knew that she was searching for tactful words. "If I were you," she presently continued, "I wouldn't tag after Hugh."

Tag! Did she call that being tactful?

"Why Mother, I ——"

"I know, dear. You only meant to be friendly."

This wholesale friendliness of Janie's had caused Mother many an embarrassing moment. "But it isn't considerate."

"What do you mean?" Janie looked straight up into Mother's eyes.

"Well, dear ——" The direct gaze of Janie's eyes had also, at times, proved an embarrassment to Mother. "He may not want ——"

"Did he tell you that?" Janie felt a hot flush creeping into her cheeks.

"Of course not." Mother closed the lid of her sewing basket and gathered up scraps of lilac tulle. "But he may feel that he has to be polite. I just wouldn't do it," she finished as though that settled the matter.

But it didn't settle the matter. For a long time after Mother had gone into the house Janie lay on the grass, her arms folded under her head, her eyes gazing up through the catalpa leaves into the blue of the summer sky. Did Hugh think she had been tagging? she wondered miserably. He hadn't seemed to mind. She thought he had rather enjoyed the things they had done together. Not as much as she had, of course. That wasn't to be expected. But, at least, he had seemed amused. Was he only being polite?

She recalled the Fourth of July when he had brought home Roman candles and rockets and pinwheels and they had set them off to the frenzied delight of all the children in the Square. Hugh

had thought that was fun, sending the rockets whizzing through the tree-tops, watching the pin-wheels
whirl in a circle of sputtering sparks . . .

"This is great, young fellow."

"The children like it, Hugh."

"Don't you?"

"I feel like a pin-wheel myself."

"Funny! So do I . . ."

The Saturday night dances at the club. She
hadn't "tagged" then. She had introduced him to
Kay Leland and Dolly Bruce and all the Manor
street girls. She had urged him to dance with
them . . .

"Sue Reid is a marvellous dancer, Hugh."

"Trying to shake me, huh?"

"You've danced with me twice already."

"Didn't you like it?"

"Uh huh!"

"Come on, then, and don't talk back to your
elders . . ."

He hadn't seemed to think she was "tagging"
when they went out to have tea at "Sportsman's
Hall" with Aunt Lucy and Muriel and Muriel's
Washington guests. It was he who had suggested
that they slip away up into the woods behind the
gardens and the stables.

"We oughtn't to, Hugh. It isn't polite."

"So much elegant conversation makes my head
ache."

"They're your kind of girls."

"My kind?"

"They've all been abroad and had coming out parties and ——"

"It hasn't done them much good . . . What is it smells so grand?"

"Sassafras. You dig up the roots and ——"

"Come on, Brownie, let's dig."

Swimming out on the point beyond the White Marsh creek. They took a picnic-supper sometimes. You could swing from the limbs of a hickory tree out and down into the water. Hugh had seemed to enjoy that . . .

"How's this, young fellow?"

"Nothing to crow about. Watch me."

"You landed flat on your tum!"

"I didn't either. That was a beautiful dive."

"Let's eat. We have to be back by seven."

"I wish we didn't."

"So do I. Here. See how far you can throw my watch."

There were other things to remember; having supper with Uncle Charlie under the tree in his weedy side yard, suppers that were fun because of Jeff's soft crabs and Uncle Charlie's remarks; sitting sometimes in the evening beside the fountain in the Square with the hurdy-gurdy playing and the locust blossoms smelling so sweet it made you want to cry; taking half a dozen youngsters to the circus, buying them pop-corn and ice-cream cones and lovely scarlet balloons . . .

Then there was the night she had driven with Hugh out to the Hollis farm. One of the men had caught his arm in a farm machine. She had helped Hugh with the bandages, gritting her teeth, feeling sick, forcing herself to look at that dreadfully mangled arm. He hadn't thought she was "tagging" then . . .

"You're a soldier, Janie."

"I liked helping you, Hugh."

"Feel all right?"

"Just sort of wobbly, that's all."

"Bless you, baby. I'll have you presented with two gold medals to-morrow morning at five o'clock." . . .

But maybe Mother knew. Perhaps he was only being polite. "Tagging." Janie felt hot with shame from her head to the tips of her toes. She flopped over on the grass and buried her face in her arms.

After that she avoided him.

"Let's go to the movies to-night."

"No thank you, Hugh." Very primly. "I have another engagement."

Or—

"I'm driving out to the Hollis farm. Want to go, young fellow?"

"I'm busy." Swallowing hard to banish a lump in her throat. "I'm going upstairs to write."

But she didn't write. She sat on the sill of the dormer window with the locust branches brushing against the screen, lonely and miserable, growing up inside. . . . "Janie cares so terribly" . . . It was silly to care about things. But you couldn't help it if that was the way you were made . . .

Hugh wondered what had happened.

"See here, small person," he said finding her picking mint leaves in the garden one afternoon. "I want to talk to you."

"I'd better go dress for supper." Janie clutched at a straw.

"No you don't!" He barred with his outstretched arms the only path to escape. "You've been dodging me for a week. I've got you now." He lifted her to the top of the wall. "You can't get away. Tell me, Janie." He wasn't smiling. His eyes looked worried and, somehow, hurt. "What stupid thing have I done?"

"Nothing."

"I've missed you, little fellow."

"I've been right here." A lump in her throat. Tears on her lashes. A desperate resolve not to let them spill down on her cheeks. "You've seen me every day."

"Not you," he said gently. "Just a linen frock and a pair of sunburned legs . . . Please tell me. If I've done anything, I'm sorry."

"I thought." She made an effort to be casual. "I was afraid you'd think I was ——" She paused, swallowed hard, spoke the humiliating word. "I was afraid you would think I was tagging."

"Tagging!"

He hadn't thought so at all. She could tell by his look of surprise. A weight lifted from her heart. She felt like a fluff of thistledown all ready to blow away. It was easy, now, to explain.

"Well, living right here with us ——" The words were tumbling all over each other. "You might have thought you had to take me places and do everything I suggested whether you wanted to or not and," she finished abruptly, "I didn't want to be a pest."

"A pest!" He disposed of the unpleasant word. "Why Janie, I've enjoyed everything. I couldn't have stayed if you hadn't been here to scold me and take me swimming and make me toe the mark. Where did you get that idea?"

"I just thought it up." She couldn't tell him that it had been Mother's idea. Anyway, what did it matter?

"You'd better stop thinking . . . Are we friends again?"

Janie nodded.

"Well that's a relief!" He drew a long gusty sigh. "To-night we'll celebrate. We'll drive out to Riverside Park."

"And have supper at the Inn?" Janie was Janie, getting excited again.

"Chicken and waffles and ginger ice-cream."

"And shoot clay pigeons?"

"And ride on the Ferris wheel."

Hugh was smiling. Janie smiled, too. She gave a little bounce of happiness and smiled her wide gay smile.

"That's the girl!" His eyes admired her. "You're lovely when you smile."

Lovely! She couldn't stop smiling.

"I feel like the Cheshire cat," she said. "Just nothing at all but a smile."

III

The Ferris wheel circled twice; up through the shadowy tree tops, down into the dazzle of lights. The third time up, it stopped; the stars very close above them, the ground very far below.

"Is something the matter, Hugh?"

"They'll fix it in a moment."

"We—we're pretty high up."

"Frightened?"

"N-o-o ——"

"You don't seem quite sure."

His arm circled around her. Her hand slipped into his. He held it close in a warm comforting clasp. Her cheek brushed his shoulder. Somewhere music was playing; up over-head were the stars. Janie was conscious of a new and bewildering emotion. "I must be falling in love," she thought. "I'm falling in love with Hugh." . . .

The wheel began to turn. She wondered if he were feeling it too, this aching, blissful emotion.

They slipped down from the shadows into the dazzle of light. He lifted her out of the car, still holding fast to her hand. What was he thinking? She glanced up at him shyly, her lashes misted with tears. He was looking at her hand.

"Janie Ballard!" he said. "You've chewed that thumb nail down to the quick!"

※ V ※

I

AUNT LUCY was having a garden party at
"Sportsman's Hall." The party was not
confined exclusively to the garden, however. In fact,
no one visited the gardens at all unless led there
by Uncle Frank to admire his peacocks, his gold-fish
or his roses. Uncle Frank boasted that each bud
on the luxuriant bushes cost him, all things considered, exactly one dollar apiece.

Uncle Frank boasted about a great many things.
He was a square thick-set man with a ruddy complexion, twenty years older than Aunt Lucy who
had pure white hair, young brown eyes and a beautiful figure. All the Ballards turned gray early in
life. Aunt Lucy had been clever enough not to
tamper with nature. Her hair was effective with
her frocks of tinted chiffon. She had the appearance of being constantly dressed and wigged for a
costume party. You liked to look at Aunt Lucy.

Uncle Frank, on the contrary, appeared always
to be dressed for a tussle with one of his horses.
He called himself a "gentleman farmer." Great-

uncle Charlie contended that the title was inaccurate. Uncle Frank Grove, he said, was neither a gentleman nor a farmer. Great-uncle Charlie was permitted to say such things merely because nobody on earth could stop him.

Great-uncle Charlie sat in a rustic chair beneath a copper-beech tree on the rolling front lawn. He was resplendent to-day in pearl gray trousers, a gaudy cravat and the swallow tailed coat that was rusty with age and shiny at all the seams. Aunt Lucy, seated with a group of her guests under a neighboring copper-beech, at intervals cast an anxious eye in his direction. She had hoped that he wouldn't be present. There was never any telling what the dreadful old man might do or say. Great-uncle Charlie was aware of her anxiety. It helped him to endure the boredom of what he considered a very stupid party.

The armchair was placed conveniently near the punch bowl. Merely by reaching out his arm Jeff was able to refill Great-uncle Charlie's glass. Jeff had been borrowed for the occasion. He was small and spry, as brown and as wrinkled as a sun-dried fig. With his tails and his buttons and his claret-colored broadcloth he looked for all the world like a hand-organ monkey as old as Time itself. Aunt Lucy borrowed Jeff on all state occasions. She apparently felt that a family servant added atmosphere even though he was not, strictly speaking, attached to her own ménage.

"How dat punch, Mistah Cha'lie?" Jeff asked as he once again performed the agreeable ceremony of refilling Great-uncle Charlie's glass.

"Tolerable, Jeff, tolerable.   Punch isn't what it used to be when we were young and handsome."

"Dat's so, Mistah Cha'lie."   Jeff's monkey face was slit by a toothless grin.   "Seem lak it done lost its persuasion."

"Exactly."   Great-uncle Charlie raised his glass aloft and smiled his waggish smile.   "Well, here's to mules and the Civil War!"

"You mustn't, Uncle Charlie."   A small determined person in a creamy frock planted herself in front of him and reached for the upraised glass.

Great-uncle Charlie twinkled at his favorite grand-neice.

"And why not, Janie my dear?"

"It's bad for your arteries, or whatever it is that hardens."

"Now, Janie.   I've had only one or two."

"It won't do you any good to fib."   A small tanned forefinger wagged reprovingly.   "Every time I've looked this way you've been either lifting a glass or setting it down."   She took the glass from his hand and placed it on the table.   "No more for him, Jeff," she said firmly.

"No ma'am, Miss Janie."   Jeff was as solemn as Death.   "Not narry anudder drap."

"I have to amuse myself with something," Great-uncle Charlie's voice was ludicrously plaintive. "I'm bored enough to drink cambric tea."

"I'll talk to you." Janie dropped down on the grass and rested her head against the trunk of the tree. "But first I'm going to scold."

Great-uncle Charlie twinkled more brightly than ever.

"That's a pretty dress," he said in his own most flattering tone.

"Isn't it?" Janie smoothed the folds of creamy chiffon, the embroidered flowers on the deep border around the hem, bluebells and rose-buds and tiny yellow daisies interwoven with sprays of green. "Aunt Lucy brought it from Paris. But you can't bribe me with ——"

"And the slippers," Great-uncle Charlie commented admiringly.

Janie stretched them out straight in front of her, tiny creamy kid slippers tied with butterfly bows.

"Hugh gave them to me for a birthday present." It was funny, Great-uncle Charlie thought, how the child lighted up sometimes. "They came from New York," she continued. "Mother said he shouldn't have but Father said it was all right. And now ——"

"I do admire a pretty foot," the old man remarked but Janie this time, was not to be diverted.

"It isn't polite of you, Uncle Charlie," she scolded, "to talk about mules and the Civil War when you're half drowned in Uncle Frank's punch."

Uncle Frank's father, it seemed, had made a fortune in shady transactions with mules during the Civil War. It was Great-uncle Charlie's favorite story. He laughed all over. His round paunch quivered. So did his shoulders and his fat pink cheeks.

"Simple gratitude, Janie my dear," he chuckled. "If mules can produce all this ——" His sweeping gesture included the glorified farm-house, the oaks and the beech-trees, the lawns and river itself, sparkling and blue in the sunshine. "Well, I'm for them, that's all. My sainted Aunt Maria!" He suddenly exclaimed. "Now what does Lucy think of that?"

Janie's eyes followed his to an oak tree along the drive. Muriel, standing, leaned against the massive trunk, her rosy skirt blowing back from her graceful legs. In one hand she held by a loop of velvet a wide-brimmed hat of lacy straw and the sunshine slipping through the somber foliage of the tree brightened her waved dark hair. Muriel, ordinarily, was not pretty, though she had Aunt Lucy's beautiful figure and warm brown eyes. Her features were heavy. But her wide square mouth had a certain charm and she dressed in exquisite taste. To-day she looked almost pretty as she leaned against the tree talking with unaccustomed vivacity to Tom McAllister, only a little taller than she.

"Aunt Lucy needn't worry, I guess," Janie said gravely.

"Wouldn't there be an explosion!" Great-uncle Charlie twinkled wickedly.

"Aunt Lucy needn't worry," Janie repeated. "Tom wouldn't know Muriel was alive if Celia were here." Her eyes strayed down over the lawn to the road along the river. Hugh had promised to come . . .

The old man made amusing remarks about the guests. Janie listened with only half of her attention. The other half waited on tip-toe for the rattle and racket of a noisy little roadster. Hugh had said he would certainly come . . .

Muriel presently strolled by with Tom McAllister.

"We're going in to dance," Muriel said in her careful finishing-school voice.

"Come along, Janie." Tom added pleasantly.

She glanced up at him. He was very good-looking, she thought, with the blue-black hair and deep blue eyes of his Irish mother combined with his grandfather's rugged features.

"No thank you, Tom." It was more pleasant to watch the road dappled over with shadows.

"When do you expect Celia?"

A shade of annoyance slipped across Muriel's face. She wasn't pretty now. She was merely a thin, rather sallow girl with a flair for the right sort of clothes.

"Soon," Janie answered. "Almost any day."

Almost any day! Janie's eyes returned to the road along the river, as Muriel and Tom strolled on toward the house. It seemed doubly important, now, that Hugh should keep his promise. Celia spoiled things for everybody. Once she, too, had believed the Celia myths. That was a long time ago.

"No thank you," she said to a maid with a tray of sandwiches.

"You aren't eating anything, Janie my dear." The words were muffled. Great-uncle Charlie had not slighted the pretty maid's tray.

"I don't feel hungry at all."

Whatever has happened to Janie? the old man wondered, and slyly reached out his glass towards the punch bowl.

Father was playing croquet. His partner was the rector's wife from the Square, plump dowdy Mrs. Warden, her eye-glasses dangling from a chain, her hair in wisps, her plackets gaping wherever a placket could gap. The rector in his rusty cleric, tall and gaunt with a lean scholarly face and an abstracted manner, had for his partner Aunt Rhoda's Ellen, a healthy young hoyden with a wind-blown bob. Aunt Rhoda, Clubs and Boards temporarily forgotten, and Brad, her ten-year-old son completed the sextette. Their voices became confused in Janie's mind with Great-uncle Charlie's comments.

"Sock it, Uncle John!"

"Rhoda is putting on weight."

"You're dead on me, Mrs. Warden."

"Those Wardens look more and more every day like Mr. and Mrs. Jack Spratt."

"I'm a rover! I'm a rover!"

"Gracious! Don't shout so, Ellen!"

"Come on, Janie," Father called when he had won the game by clicking Mrs. Jack Spratt's ball against the post. "We'll whitewash Ellen and Brad."

"It's too warm, Father. I don't feel like playing now."

Whatever has happened to Janie? Great-uncle Charlie wondered again. Usually at the sound of her father's voice she lighted up like a candle. He glanced down at his favorite grandniece, brown as a beech-nut in her creamy embroidered frock. She sat very still, with a sort of a listening look, her eyes on the road from town. A ray of light pricked through the mist of questions in Great-uncle Charlie's head.

"What time is it, Uncle Charlie?"

The old man consulted a ponderous watch.

"Half past four."

Half past four! If something had happened to Hugh!

Mother, very pretty in blue lace, walked by with pompous Mrs. Leland. There was a glow about Mother to-day. She did so enjoy parties and dressing up and maids serving sandwiches and a limousine or two standing along a curving drive.

"I'd *love* to serve on *your* committee," Mother was saying to Mrs. Leland whose limousine was larger and more magnificent than any of the others.

Poor Mother! She hated it so to live in the shabby old Square.

Uncle Frank sauntered by in his baggy tweeds, smoking a fat cigar. The gentleman farmer. Heavy jowls, ruddy complexion, thick grizzled hair.

"Hello, Uncle Charlie. Want to have a look at the peacocks?"

"I can see them from here."

Great-uncle Charlie was looking at the Lucas girls, stringy, over-dressed, talking shrilly, laughing at nothing at all.

"Uncle Charlie Ballard!" Janie scolded affectionately. "You're a perfectly dreadful old man!"

Her attention, momentarily diverted, returned to the road along the river. If something had happened to Hugh . . .

And then she heard it, the clatter and racket of a noisy little roadster. Instantly she was alive all over, eyes shining, words tumbling, creamy kid slippers dancing with excitement.

"That's Horatius! He's come, Uncle Charlie! He's come!"

"Who's come—Santa Claus?"

"Hugh! But he isn't coming in. He's waiting and tooting the horn. Isn't it a silly horn, Uncle

Charlie? It sounds like a cat with the croup. Oh my goodness! I'd better go see what's happened."

Great-uncle Charlie watched her race down the drive, skirt blowing, legs twinkling, the butterfly bows on her slippers lifting like tiny wings. The first faint ray of suspicion became as the breaking of dawn.

"So that's the way the wind blows," Great-uncle Charlie observed to Jeff. "When Celia comes home there'll be ructions. My sainted Aunt Maria! I wish—I hope I'll be asleep!"

II

"Aren't you glad I kidnapped you?" Hugh, in his bathing suit, lay among the moss and pine needles on the bank at the tip of the point.

"You didn't, exactly." Janie, sitting on a blanket to protect her party frock, gave a little bounce of pleasure. "I just came tagging along."

"Well, anyway, we're here." Hugh stretched lazily. "Was it a nice party?"

"Uncle Charlie drank all the punch."

"Did he?" Hugh laughed. "He's a grand old boy . . . And what did you do, Janie?"

"I sat on the grass with my feet stretched out so people would admire my slippers."

"Did they?"

"I didn't notice," she confessed. "I was so busy admiring them myself."

"You baby," he said. "You dear little funny kid."

Janie's spirits dropped for a moment. She felt particularly grown up and elegant in the frock of creamy chiffon which Aunt Lucy had brought from Paris. Funny kid! Even the "dear" didn't help very much. Hugh would persist in treating her like a child and he, she reflected, was no more than a boy himself with his tempers and whistling and spells of being lazy. Sometimes she felt like his mother. He scattered things all over the house and never could find his hat. It was, "Janie, where's this, and where's that?" dozens of times a day. There he was now, chinning himself on a hickory limb and looking to see if she didn't think he was grand.

"How's that?"   Expectantly.

"You baby!"   Tilting her chin in the air.

"Imp!"

He swung into the water, pulled away from the shore with long even strokes. Janie sighed with content. Lovely day! The river was blue and shining. The sun was setting and the puffy clouds were dyed in tints of pink. There were birds in the scraggly pine-trees and soft little cheeping sounds. Something smelled spicy and fragrant. Those tiny red berries perhaps. Wintergreen.

Hugh had swum out so far that his head was a glint in the distance. The current was strong. If something should happen to Hugh! There, thank goodness, he was stroking it back to the shore. Presently he waded in to the bank, bronzed and healthy, shaking the water in a shower of shining drops from his copper-gold hair.

"The water's great!"

"Hugh! You shouldn't swim out so far."

"Why not?"

She couldn't tell him exactly why. It was all mixed up with the wintergreen smell and the puffy pink clouds, with the singing inside of her heart.

"Funerals are a nuisance," she said. "And I look dreadful in black."

He laughed and threw himself down beside her, his head on the olive-green blanket.

"Light me a cigarette."

"You're the laziest person I know."

"My hands are wet."

She lit it, of course, puffed once or twice and promptly handed it over. They talked. Hugh discussed his hazy plans for the future.

"I think I'll go abroad for a year or two."

"You've been, haven't you?"

"Pleasure jaunts with Louise and Rod." He disposed of such frivolity. "To study, I mean. Berlin and Vienna."

Berlin! Vienna! Janie felt lost and forlorn.

"That little Miss Ellie looks sick to me." Hugh had returned to the Square and Janie felt happy again. "She ought not to run a sewing-machine all day and all night."

"They're poor, Hugh. They have to live on just what Miss Ellie makes."

"Why doesn't she marry that fellow in the store? I should think it would simplify matters?"

"Mrs. Pope says she would rather see her dead."

"She probably will. Old harridan! Gee, you have pretty feet."

An interval of silence. The pink in the sky a clear pale amethyst now. Shadows creeping among the trees.

"Janie."

"Hmm?"

"I thought you had gone to sleep."

"I was thinking."

"What?"

"Do you hate it terribly, Hugh?"

"Hate what, you funny kid?"

"Living with us in the Square."

"No. I like it . . . And say, I'm crashing into society. Tony Silver's wife invited me to the new Silver's christening party."

"Shall you go?"

"If you'll go with me. And what about a present? Will you get me something gorgeous?"

"A silver cup with the name engraved?"

"Better make it a keg. The name is Victor Emanuel Sebastian—I can't remember the rest."

Another interval of silence.

"Did I tell you the General broke his leg?"

"Oh Hugh! Is he suffering much?"

"Not excessively." A chuckle of amusement. "It was the peg-leg that cracked."

"Oh!" A low little throaty gurgle. "Where will he get a new one?"

"The old lady seems to think the Lord will provide."

"Meaning Father, I suppose . . . Hugh, we ought to be getting home."

"It's pleasant here . . . Light me another fag."

"Your hands are perfectly dry."

"But you do it so well." A teasing smile. "They always taste better somehow."

"You're a pampered young man."

"And you are a good little egg."

Egg! A lady in a Paris frock! A long indignant silence.

"Janie."

"Hmm?"

"We could have a Christmas party for the kids in the Square."

"What made you think of Christmas?"

"That star up there above the tallest pine."

A tiny star shining alone in the primrose and amethyst sky . . . They planned a Christmas party for the children in the Square. Janie remembered with a pang that three months of the time between this evening and Christmas she would be in college three hundred miles away. She spoke of it dolefully. Hugh promised to come for a week-end and write to her very often. That made it seem less of a trying ordeal. Funny to feel that way. She had liked college pretty well . . .

The twilight inspired confidences. Hugh told Janie about his childhood. The sketches he drew were pathetic, Janie thought, remembering the Square as it used to be. Hugh hadn't known any-thing about Christmas with uncles and aunts and cousins coming for dinner, a tree lighted with real candles and holly wreaths in all the windows. He hadn't known about birthday surprises and picnics down the river and playing theatre in the attic when it rained. He hadn't, apparently, known anything about home.

"Dad was always busy," he explained. "I never really knew him until after my brother was killed."

"How old were you then?"

"Ten. Dad blamed himself, I think. He felt that he had neglected Owen and given him too much money. He wanted to do better by me. When he found he couldn't finish the job, he turned me over to your father. He didn't trust Louise. Leading a useful life, to her, is a very quaint idea."

Janie longed to say something helpful and grown-up and wise. She couldn't think of a single thing. So she slipped her hand into his and said nothing at all.

He talked to her seriously about the things he

wanted to do. "As though I were more important," she thought, "than just a funny kid." She wished it needn't end, this feeling of being close to him, sharing his dreams, planning things for the future. Maybe, some time, he would feel it too, this closeness, this wishing it needn't end. Mother had married Father when she was just nineteen . . .

"Look at our Christmas tree now," Hugh suddenly exclaimed.

The tallest pine was tipped with a brilliant new star.

"You can't see the tiny first one," Janie mourned. "It's lost in the dazzle."

Lost in the dazzle! That's how it is with Celia and me, Janie thought miserably. The tiny star had looked so lovely alone . . .

The twilight had deepened. Everything seemed hushed and shadowed and almost heart-breakingly sad. Lost in the dazzle! It was always that way. No use to hope that this time it would be different. Janie tried to win back the tears that gathered on her lashes. The attempt was unsuccessful. They rolled forlornly over her cheeks, splashed down on Hugh's hand in her lap.

"Are you crying, Janie?"

A negative shake of her head.

"What is it, little fellow?"

"I—I feel sort of chilly. Hugh, please take me home."

III

Horatius stopped, with his customary protest, in front of the old brick house. Janie, waiting on the sidewalk for Hugh to find his bag, saw a spurt of light in the living-room and then through the buff-tinted blinds a soft and flickering glow. Mother must have callers. But why was she lighting the candles? It seemed a little odd.

"I'm about to perish from famine," Hugh said as they opened the front door. "Do you suppose we can raid the ice-box?"

"There probably isn't much. Rachel thought we'd have tea at Aunt Lucy's."

Janie paused to smooth her hair in the mirror above the card-tray table. Hugh walked on down the hall.

"A lone sardine ——" He did not complete the sentence.

Janie turned. He had halted at the living-room door and seemed rooted to the spot. Janie walked to his side, looked in through the portieres and buried her fondest dreams.

Celia, in misty white, sat at the piano, her chin a little raised to show the long lovely curve of her throat. Her hair, parted demurely in the middle and twisted into a knot at the nape of her neck, was the color of new strained honey. The candle-light made a radiance about her head and gave her skin the translucent quality of thin creamy porcelain. She appeared to be wrapped in reveries and totally unconscious of observing eyes.

Hugh's tribute to the picture was almost soundless, a quick indrawn breath. But Janie heard it. Celia, as though she had heard it too, turned with a pretty start of surprise. Her violet eyes lost, for a moment, their dreaming expression. Her lips curved in a gentle welcoming smile.

"Janie," she murmured in a voice like plucked silver harp-strings. "It's lovely to see you again."

Janie drew a long deep breath and gallantly lifted her chin.

"Celia," she said, "this is Hugh."

VI

I

CELIA was at home. It made everything different. Janie was seldom allowed to forget that she was merely the plain little sister of the prettiest girl in town. Not that Celia was unkind to Janie. She was, on the contrary, very sweet and affectionate. "Janie is devoted to that playground," she would say in the presence of a caller. "She's such a busy brown little bee. She makes me feel like a butterfly." Bees, of course, are dull little creatures and butterflies are enchanting. Celia was kind to Janie. She brought her a box of salt water taffy from the shore and a necklace made out of shells.

It made everything different. The old brick house came to life as though someone had kissed a princess. The telephone seemed always to be ringing. The side porch was of no use at all so far as the family was concerned. Celia was a belle. Celia was what gallant elderly gentlemen called a "toast." Celia, in short, was the prettiest girl in town.

"I never saw anything like it," Aunt Rhoda mar

veled to Mother. They were having tea in the living-room. Janie was reading in the hall. Celia had just been whirled off by the Manor street crowd for a supper party somewhere.

"Celia is popular," Mother said in a tone of pardonable pride.

"But the girls are fond of her, too." Aunt Rhoda's Ellen was just fourteen. Aunt Rhoda had much to learn. "Do you remember how we loathed Sallie Harper because the boys were crazy about her?"

"You invited her just the same." Great-uncle Charlie, too, was having a cup of tea. "You had to. The bees and the honey jar. The moth and the flickering flame."

"Sallie Harper was a conceited minx." Mother's voice rebuked them both for presuming to compare her Celia with the belle of a past generation. "Celia is nice to everybody. She has a beautiful disposition."

Great-uncle Charlie made a spluttering sound as though he had been forced to laugh at an inconvenient moment.

"Damn it, Helen!" he said. "This tea is infernally hot!"

Celia, just at first, paid little attention to Hugh. Janie wondered at her lack of appreciation. She wanted her to admire him—from a safe and disinterested distance.

"Isn't he nice?" she asked one evening. She was

watching Celia dress in her airy front bedroom
upstairs, all lilac and cream and rose, as fresh and
as dainty as Celia herself.

"He looks healthy." Celia was absorbed in the
pretty task of brushing her silky hair.

"I think he's nice-looking." Janie's cheeks were
unusually pink. "And he's getting along so well.
Father says Hugh is a born doctor."

"I've had enough of doctors!" Celia's voice was
almost petulant.

"Why Celia Ballard!" Janie's eyes were blazing.

"Father is different, of course." Celia hastened
to make amends. She had to be approved of—even
by brown little Janie. "But the atmosphere de-
presses me so, sickness and suffering and pain. You
wouldn't understand, Janie dear. You don't mind
such things. I'm so absurdly sensitive."

From which Janie gathered, with a lifting of her
spirits, that Celia had no ambition to be a doctor's
wife.

Celia, however, was aware of Hugh. Janie knew
that very well. Often she sat at the old-fashioned
square piano wearing what Janie called her "Saint
Cecelia" expression. Hugh was fond of music.
Celia would talk to him about Chopin preludes and
the haunting waltzes of Strauss. But her fingers
would continue to hover above the keys, content
with striking here and there a single soft note. Celia
could not have played "Chop-sticks" without a great

deal of concentration. But you couldn't tell Hugh.
It wasn't a thing you could possibly say.

Janie talked to him about Celia.

"She's pretty, isn't she?" she asked as they were
riding home from the playground one afternoon.

"Lovely. She has beautiful bones."

"What a gruesome thought!" And then, very
wistfully, a moment later, "Do I have pretty
bones?"

Hugh laughed and teased her about her tan.

"You belong in Shantytown with the rest of the
shines."

"I'll start in to-night using cucumber cream."

"Don't you dare! I like that dusky bloom."

Janie felt happy and contented. He liked her
even if she was solemn-looking and brown.

The feeling of happiness vanished, however, when
she saw him standing in the hall late that afternoon
watching Celia walk down the stairs. Celia wore a
frock of sheer white swiss with a tight bodice and
a full ankle-length skirt. At her waist was a small
corsage of lilies-of-the-valley tied with loops of
green ribbon. She was, Janie herself was forced
to admit, too lovely to be real. She saw the admiring expression in Hugh's brown eyes, heard his
quick indrawn breath.

"That's the way I thought of you," he said
softly. "Lilies-of-the-valley."

Janie didn't wait to hear any more. She rushed
out through the kitchen, up the back stairs, along the

second floor hall and up to her own quiet room. It was a peaceful haven, comforting and familiar. She flung herself face down on the bed and cried a little and kicked at the counterpane with her toes. Then she felt better. She bathed her eyes and smoothed her hair and began to dress for supper.

At supper, Hugh talked very little. He kept looking at Celia, all white and creamy and pink with her honey-colored head set like a flower on the slender stem of her throat. Celia, also, talked very little. She appeared to be wrapped in reveries. Her long-lashed violet eyes seemed to be gazing upon some hidden loveliness beyond the restricted vision of ordinary mortals. She refused second helpings, and, at intervals, she smiled.

"I'm glad you didn't get yourself sunburned." Mother, too, was looking at Celia, all white and creamy and pink. "Janie looks like a gypsy."

Father was looking at Janie.

"I like gypsy girls," he said with a quick warm smile.

Janie felt a lump in her throat. Father, she thought, was the dearest person in all the world.

II

It made everything different, Celia being at home. Muriel invited them out for tea, Celia and Janie and Hugh. This time Hugh didn't suggest that they slip away up into the woods. He sat on the

lawn and looked at Celia in her wide-brimmed lilac
hat. Janie sat on the grass hugging her knees in
her arms as silent as a small bronze statue. Muriel
smoked cigarettes and looked decidedly bored.
Celia talked about herself and had a beautiful time.

Tom McAllister joined them presently. He had
been talking legal affairs in the house with Uncle
Frank. Tom drew up a wicker chair and he, too,
looked at Celia in her wide-brimmed lilac hat. Hugh,
occasionally, made an effort to include Janie and
Muriel in the conversation. Tom looked at Celia,
a quizzical smile twisting the left corner of his
mouth. It was a smile which seemed to say, "I am
not deceived by your poses but I think you are
beautiful." Tom always looked at Celia that way.

Tom had an Irish mother and a Scotch father.
It was the Irish in him, Muriel said, which wor-
shipped Celia's beauty. The canny Scotch part of
him kept him from being deceived. You wondered
which was stronger. Perhaps Tom wondered, too.

It was amazing, Janie thought, how Celia com-
manded attention. She never said anything witty
or beautiful or wise. You expected her to, when
she sat with her hands linked loosely in her lap,
her eyes dreaming off into the distance. Perhaps
that was the reason. You waited for a glimpse of
the hidden loveliness which Celia promised. She
had a gift for ensnaring the imagination. It worked
out very well.

Muriel, her graceful figure meshed in a web of

knitted silk, talked indolently of a recent trip to Japan.

"There was a Japanese man at our hotel," Celia interrupted. "He called me Almond Flower." She laughed softly, a single quivering harp string.

That was the way she did it, Janie thought. She made you feel that the almond trees in far Japan had flowered for the sole purpose of giving Celia a pretty name. She saw the flash of interest in Hugh's brown eyes and wished she had never been born.

Muriel talked no further of Japan. Tom asked Janie about the playground.

"I think it's dear of Janie to be interested in those little foreigners." Celia smiled at her small grave sister. "She makes me feel absolutely worthless. I adore children. They were so cunning on the beach in their wisps of bathing suits. I used to build castles for them. We played fairy tales. They pretended that I was the Princess."

Janie knew that Hugh had no mental vision of Janie struggling with dirty little foreigners. He saw Celia beneath an umbrella on the beach, building castles for pretty clean children who called her "Princess." He saw her, perhaps, with his own children, red-haired boys who looked like Hugh, tiny blonde girls with Celia's violet eyes. It worked out very well.

A maid brought tea and sandwiches and small round cakes in cups of fluted paper.

"Aren't they cunning," Celia asked, "in their ruffled petticoats?"

Hugh smiled his appreciation. Tom dropped two lumps of sugar in Celia's cup. Muriel and Janie exchanged a long expressive glance.

Hugh was reminded of a servant they'd had who told fortunes with tea leaves.

"I had my fortune told at the shore." Celia's manner made it seem a remarkable achievement. "A crystal gazer. She told me I was psychic. She said she felt it the moment I entered the room. I do have strange premonitions sometimes. I feel them in my wrists. Little stabs like rose pricks."

Celia and Hugh and Tom talked about premonitions. Muriel lit a fresh cigarette. Janie continued to wish that she had never been born.

Tom presently glanced at Muriel, lying back in the low wicker chair, her long graceful legs indolently crossed, the smoke from the cigarette wreathing above her head.

"You look like an ad for Chesterfields," he said.

"Doesn't she?" Hugh agreed.

"Muriel is so sophisticated." Celia smiled prettily. "I wish I didn't look like a lace-paper valentine," she added with a quivering sigh.

"Excuse me." Muriel rose from her chair and walked toward the house. Janie followed, after a moment. She made no apologies. It wasn't necessary. Celia was talking about herself. No one noticed that Janie had gone.

Muriel was pacing back and forth in the wide oak-beamed hall.

"If I had stayed, I would have thrown things," she said to Janie.

Muriel looked almost ugly to-day. Her face was somber; her eyes were dark with helpless rage. Janie thought of the garden party when Muriel had looked pretty, standing against the oak-tree, talking and laughing with Tom. She thought of running away with Hugh to the point beyond the White Marsh creek. She remembered how he had smiled at her and told her all of his dreams . . .

"Look at our Christmas tree now!"

"You can't see the tiny first star."

"It's lost in the dazzle." . . .

Janie looked at Muriel.

"It makes everything different," she said, "Celia being at home."

III

Celia cherished a secret. It had to do with square gray envelopes which arrived at irregular intervals.

"Who is it, darling?" Mother would ask. She liked to enjoy, vicariously, her pretty daughter's conquests.

"Just someone I met at the shore." Celia would smile mysteriously as though there were some things in life too sacred to be discussed.

Janie wondered about it. Celia, usually, made a

grand parade of her victims. Could Celia have fallen in love? That, somehow, was a strange idea. You thought of people falling in love with Celia.

His name was Carter. Janie found a half-finished letter on Celia's cream and ivory desk.

Carter dear—

It's dreadful to be so sensitive. Nobody understands. Last night I went out and stood in the garden. The wind sighed through the trees and all the roses were still. I felt small and lost and alone. If you had been here—

Last night Celia had returned home late from a dance at the club and fallen asleep as soon as her head touched the pillow. Janie felt like adding a post-script to the letter. She nobly refrained.

It was Great-aunt Rose who explained. She came to call one Sunday afternoon. Great-aunt Rose was a brittle old lady with very bright blue eyes. Her skin looked like the under side of white rose petals which have turned a little brown. She sat on the living-room davenport, her jeweled old hands folded on the crook of an ebony cane. Celia was spending the day with Aunt Rhoda. Janie sat curled up with a book in a fat leather chair. Mother rocked languidly and waved a palm-leaf fan.

"I suppose Celia has told you, Helen," Aunt Rose began.

"Has something happened?" Mother, of course, was expecting the worst.

"Something which may be pleasant." Aunt Rose smiled faintly. She never really laughed. It wasn't aristocratic. "A charming young man, vacationing at the shore, was very attentive to our pretty little girl."

"From Washington?" Mother had glimpsed the post-marks on the square gray envelopes.

"He is located in Washington now." Aunt Rose, on all occasions, spoke as though she were addressing a meeting of the D.A.R. "His home, he informed me, is in Charleston."

"What is his name?" Mother, Janie thought, was getting a little excited. Charleston! It had a fascinating sound. You thought of mansions and live-oak trees and gardens of vivid flowers . . .

"Carter Shelby." Aunt Rose gave the name her unqualified approval. "I have made investigations. The Carters and the Shelbys are prominent in Charleston society."

"And you think——" Mother was seeing visions and dreaming dreams.

"I think he was very much attracted." Aunt Rose was obviously pleased. The jet butterflies on her hat quivered with tinkling approval. "I think we are likely to lose our pretty little girl."

It was a loss which Janie felt she could bear with fortitude. Bless this Carter Shelby! If only Celia would marry him! Maybe then . . .

After that Mother ceased to look with a calculating expression at Celia and Hugh. Janie found

her rummaging one day through a book case in
the upstairs sitting-room. It harbored the literary
cast-offs of the years, baby books, "The Little
Colonel" series, "Big Game in Africa," the detective
stories that Grandfather Ballard had liked, two
rows of massive volumes which were bound copies
of the "Century" magazine. It was through these
that Mother was busily searching.

"What are you looking for?" Janie asked.

"I remember seeing it once." Mother fluttered
the pages and little puffs of dust swirled up into
the air. Janie watched and wondered. Mother,
as a rule, was not devoted to literature. "Here it
is!" she exclaimed. "Janie! Would you look!"

Janie dropped to her knees and looked over
Mother's shoulder. The article was entitled
"Charleston Gardens." There were pictures in
color of box-wood hedges and sun dials and clumps
of flaming azaleas.

"A perfect setting for Celia!" Mother murmured with visions in her eyes.

"It's lovely," Janie agreed.

"And look at this!"

Janie saw through a tunnel of arching trees a mansion of rose-red brick. Mother's finger trembled
as it pointed out the line of lettering beneath the
picture. "*Magnolia*—The Home of Colonel Valentine Shelby."

"It might not be the same one," Janie objected.

It did seem that Mother was counting a number of unhatched eggs.

"Aunt Rose never makes mistakes like that." Mother was dreaming over the picture. "I," she sighed, "will never escape this Square. But Celia certainly shall."

Celia, however, volunteered no information. She continued to act as though young Mr. Shelby was a subject too sacred to be discussed. When a square gray envelope failed to arrive in the morning mail she was petulant and plaintive. When it did arrive, she donned her "Saint Cecelia" expression. Janie wondered. Had Celia fallen in love?

Father went away for the last two weeks in August. His friend, Judge Trent, from Baltimore, had a camp in the Blue Ridge mountains. Father was pleased and excited.

"A legacy is useful," he said at breakfast the morning he left.

"I'll do my best, Doctor Ballard," Hugh promised gravely.

"Keep an eye on him, Janie."

"Both eyes, Father." Janie was perched on the arm of his chair, wanting to keep him, happy because he could go.

"Do take care of yourself, John." Mother was closing a bag. "Remember—nothing fried!"

Stoney was waiting with Father's car at the door. Rachel was announcing the time in melancholy accents. Father was kissing Mother and Janie and shaking hands with Hugh.

"Where's Celia?" he asked.

"She came in so late last night," Mother answered quickly. "I couldn't bear to wake her."

Father looked disappointed. "All right," he said. "Kiss her good-bye for me."

A chorus of good-byes. Stoney stowing Father's bags in the back of the shabby old car. Rachel wiping her eyes on her apron and grumbling for all she was worth. A waving of hands. A splutter and roar from the engine. Father was gone!

Hugh was busy after that. Shantytown languished in the heat. There was an accident at the mill. Old Mrs. Pope had a heart attack. He had no time to sit on the lawn at Aunt Lucy's and fall in love with Celia. Janie scolded him and praised him and made him lemonade. She felt almost happy again and forgot to wish she had never been born. And then—

Janie came into the garden one evening through the alley-way gate. Celia was sitting with someone on the seat around the catalpa tree. But it wasn't Hugh. It was Tom McAllister. She walked slowly across the grass, making no noise at all.

"Celia, darling," Tom was saying, "have you ever had in all your life a really honest emotion?"

"That isn't kind." The silver harp strings quivered. "You don't understand me, Tom."

"Oh, yes I do. You're a clever little lady—but not quite clever enough."

"Life is so hard for me, Tom." The harp strings were playing a tragic tune. "I simply can't bear to hurt people. Sometimes I wish I were cross-eyed and had a wart on my chin."

"Celia! Celia!" A tender, laughing rebuke. "The Irish in me wants to kiss you. The Scotch in me tells me to spank you instead. I think it's the shamrock I'm wearin'. I'll just be Irish to-night."

Janie momentarily interrupted Tom's romantic intentions. She slipped past them with a casual "hello" and walked on toward the house. Her eyes lifted to Hugh's window. The room was dark but a point of flame moved like a fire-fly across the screen. A cigarette, she thought. Was Hugh up there, watching Celia, caring because she sat with Tom McAllister beneath the catalpa tree?

Hugh's door was open when she reached the top of the stairs. He sat in the hearth-side chair with an open book in his hand. The light from the reading lamp splashed down on his touseled bright hair. There had been no light in the room before, only that point of flame.

"Hello, Janie." He smiled as she stopped at the door. "Are you sleepy, little fellow?"

"Not very." She studied his face. He looked tired, she thought, restless, unhappy.

"Let's get the Packard," he said, "and ride for a million miles."

He did care about Celia. Oh, dear big laughing Hugh . . . Janie swallowed hard.

"I'd love it," she said. "We'll ride and ride and ride."

"You're nice, Janie Ballard," Hugh said gently. "You're a very good little egg."

VII

I

CARTER SHELBY was expected at any moment!
Janie, returning from the playground one
afternoon early in September, found the old brick
house in a state of wild excitement.

"It's Celia's friend, Mr. Shelby," Mother said
in answer to Janie's question. "He's coming for
supper. The telegram arrived at noon. But we
didn't open it and Celia came home only an hour
ago. Stoney is out with Father and Hugh is freez-
ing the sherbet. Rachel is as mad as a hornet's nest
and I am simply exhausted. If you'd dust the living-
room, Janie ——"

"Where's Celia?"

"She's dressing." Mother's face was flushed.
Her hair curled in moist tendrils against her forehead. "Would you use a cloth or doilies? Aunt
Rose sent the flowers. They're fading already.
I'm afraid my icing won't harden. It never does
when I especially want it to be nice. Why haven't
we had this room papered? It really is a disgrace.

If only John Ballard would forget the widows and orphans long enough ——"

"I don't see why you make such a fuss," Janie said rather crossly.

"Can't you appreciate Celia's feelings at all?" Mother's expression implied that Janie was no true daughter of hers but an orphan found on a doorstep. "Isn't this Square bad enough with children screaming and men in their shirt sleeves and no one to serve but Rachel? If your dear father ——" Mother paused for a much needed breath. "And Celia is so sensitive ——"

"Celia is a luxury this family can't afford."

"Janie!" Mother was close to tears.

"All right. I'll polish up the handle on the old front door."

"You needn't bother with that." Mother was a literal soul and far too flurried for flights of fancy.

"I mean I'll dust the living-room. And I certainly hope that our labor is not in vain."

Janie attended to the dusting in no very amiable frame of mind. She was warm and weary. She wanted a bath. Celia would be dressing while everyone else worked like slaves. Even Hugh. She saw him turning the freezer in the shade of the catalpa tree, his collar opened, his sleeves rolled up, a smudgy streak on his nose. Dear Hugh. If Celia would marry this Carter Shelby . . . She returned to the dusting with new determination.

Celia, upstairs, was experiencing a moment or two

of utter panic. She had described it to Carter
Shelby as a charming place, this shabby old-fashioned house. She had made him see her against
a background of dim green arbors, climbing roses,
ancestral portraits and faithful family servants.
What would he think of Rachel? What would he
think of the Square? She had let him suppose that
they were wealthy. It was easy and pleasant to
create that impression, travelling with Great-aunt
Rose. You said she preferred a quiet hotel. You
asked Great-aunt Rose to wear her amethysts and
her diamond-studded combs . . .

What would he think of it all? Celia mentally
inspected the dining-room with its dingy paper and
the stains on the ceiling where the bathroom plumbing leaked through. Carter was fastidious. She
remembered that he had noticed little things. She
liked him for it. But now. If only she hadn't made
it seem like a picture. Mulberry Square! He had
liked the name. She had talked about the fountain . . .

She knew she was half way in love with him. He
was so good-looking, his ardent dark eyes, his wavy
dark hair, his charmingly graceful manners. She
hadn't been quite sure of him. In spite of the letters, she wasn't quite sure of him now. There was
an air about him, a flavor of far away places. She
wanted him to take her away from this dreary old
Square. Celia and Carter. They were handsome

together . . . "Mrs. Carter Shelby. Oh yes, the Charleston Shelbys. Lovely little thing" . . .

What should she wear? Celia, in peach-tinted lingerie, fluttered distractedly around the room. The heels of her mules tapped sharply on the floor between the rugs. She flung open her wardrobe door. This was a trying time of the year. Her summer frocks looked wilted and stringy. The white tulle? That was too formal. Janie, in all probability, would appear in linen and socks. The primrose chiffon? The lilac organdy? The lilac organdy. That was becoming. And the slippers Mother had dyed.

The organdy. She slipped it on. As her head and throat emerged from the lilac cloud, she smiled again. Did it matter, after all, that the house was shabby and needed repairs?

She sat before the triple mirror of the dressing table, smoothing her silky hair . . . "Your hair is like the wimple of some too-frivolous nun." She heard his voice, that South Carolina accent. A pleased dreamy expression crept into her eyes. She would tell him that she had exaggerated a little perhaps. The old house to her was so very dear. She couldn't fail. There was all this loveliness to help her.

"You pretty thing," she whispered to the dreaming girl in the mirror.

Hugh was standing beside the newel post as Celia walked down the stairs. She saw in his eyes a tribute to her beauty. He was much less attractive than Carter Shelby, she thought. There was no hint of mystery about this healthy red-haired young doctor. But he admired her.

"Thank you for helping, Hugh." She muted the silver harp strings. She let her hand rest for a moment on his arm.

Janie came out from the living-room. She looked sulky and cross and disheveled. Funny little brown girl! It was a shame that Janie was so plain.

"Hurry and dress, dear." Celia smiled at her grave little sister.

The dining-room looked better than she had expected with the pink and lavender cosmos and the tall pale candles. Celia lowered the shades. There! The stains on the wall scarcely showed. The kitchen was deserted. There was a smell of roast chicken. The salads were ready, crisp leaves of lettuce, red pepper rings, olive stuffed with pimentoes. The icing was just hard enough on the small round cakes. Upstairs she heard water running and Mother calling to Father. They were good to her. She would make it up to them when she had a great deal of money. It was her duty to marry well. She alone could rescue them all from this tawdry old Square. She felt noble for a moment. Joan of Arc . . .

A clock struck six. Celia wandered back into the living-room. It wasn't really so bad. The flowers pleased her. Some Oriental rugs looked

almost as faded as this. She tried to see it as
Carter would see it. What would he think of it all?
Her spirits drooped a little. She glanced into a
mirror and was instantly reassured. The shabby old
house accented her fresh young beauty. A rose in
an autumn garden . . .

Mother came downstairs, patting herself into
place. Father presently followed, Janie, Hugh.
The long hand of the clock moved to half-past six.

"Shouldn't he be here, darling?" Mother asked
anxiously.

"He didn't say any definite time."

"Coming by train?" Father was hungry and
wanted his supper.

"He's driving."

"I'm starved," Janie said with a patient sigh.

Hugh picked out notes on the piano and looked
at Celia in her lilac organdy frock. Celia listened
for the door-bell and pleated the edge of her handkerchief. Rachel appeared at the door. The
starched white frill on her head gave her the look
of an elderly cherub who was very much out of sorts.

"Supper gwine be ruined," she announced gloom-
ily, "ef you all doan eat it soon."

The door-bell rang. All eyes turned to Celia.

"You go, Rachel," she said.

Rachel returned with a telegram.

"Fo' you, Miss Celia."

Celia ripped it open, pulled out the yellow sheet.
She read it through and crumpled it in her hand.

"He isn't coming!" she cried in a passion of anger and disappointment.

"Never mind, darling." Mother's face paled.

"I can't bear it!" Celia saw that Hugh was looking at her. She felt that her face was distorted with rage. "I can't bear it for you, Mother." Her voice was plaintive again. "You've worked so dreadfully hard."

"Rats!" said Janie—but not out loud.

"It's all right." Mother was soothing Celia with soft little hushing sounds. "Don't fret."

"No use wasting a party." Father was smiling as though a tragedy had not occurred. "Call over the wall, Janie, to Doctor and Mrs. Warden."

Celia was amiable at supper. She laughed at the rector's jokes and was attentive to dowdy Mrs. Warden. But at the end of the meal her handkerchief was torn into ragged shreds.

II

The next day it rained. The house was chilly. Celia came languidly downstairs at noon. She wore an old woolen dress that was faded and out of pleat. Her eyes were heavy. She hadn't slept very well. Janie was lying flat on her stomach beside the living-room hearth. Someone had made a fire. Janie was reading and munching an apple.

"Didn't you go to the playground?" Celia asked.

"The kids aren't ducks." Janie turned a page.

"Where's Mother?"

"Having lunch with Mrs. Leland." Janie kicked her heels together. "It's a committee meeting."

"When do we have lunch?"

"We don't. Rachel is in bed with neuritis."

"Father?"

"He's gone to the city."

Celia moved restlessly around the room. How shabby it looked! No one had dusted. The flowers were drooping. Glimpsed through the rain-splattered windows the Square was dismal and forlorn. How could Janie be contented, reading beside the hearth?

"Pete Bruce 'phoned you," Janie said.

"What did he want?"

"I don't know."

Celia didn't care. Peter Bruce with his thick red hands. Was this to be her life?

The small white dog crept out of his basket, followed her around the room.

"Go away!" She said sharply and pushed with her foot at the whining creature.

Janie scrambled up from the hearth, rescued "Tweedles," tucked him back into his basket. She said nothing at all but Celia felt rebuked.

"I have a miserable headache." She drooped like a wilting flower into the chair beside the hearth.

Janie lay on her stomach, reading, munching the apple, turning a page now and then. Celia thought that she envied Janie in spite of the fact that she was solemn-looking and brown. It would be comfortable to be insensitive, not pained by shabbiness, torn into shreds of emotion. If only Carter had come . . .

Hugh came in presently. Celia brightened a little. They had a picnic lunch in front of the fire; scraps of chicken, buttered toast, cocoa and cakes. Celia sat on a foot-stool so that the firelight would shine across her hair. She talked to Hugh.

"How do you like our funny old Square?"

Hugh talked to Celia and watched the shine of the firelight on her honey-colored hair. Lovely, he thought, the curve of her throat, her delicate oval face. She would always be lovely. Her bones were beautifully formed . . .

Janie lay on the hearth rug and looked at Hugh. Celia would make him miserable, she thought, her affectations, her gift for putting every one in the wrong except herself. Hugh was sincere and honest and fine. He would worship Celia and Celia would take advantage. She didn't want Hugh to be hurt. It was miserable, being hurt. "Don't fall in love with her, Hugh. Oh, darling laughing Hugh!" . . .

The door-bell rang. Celia slipped away to answer it. A tall young man in a belted coat stood on the rain-splashed steps.

"Is this Doctor Ballard's residence?" A southern accent. Live-oak trees, azaleas, a mansion of rose-red brick . . .

"Yes." The rain was falling on his wavy dark

hair. His face was dark even when he smiled. His teeth were very white.

"Is Miss Ballard at home?"

Celia answered in person.

"Why, Carter Shelby!" The silver harp strings were tautly drawn. She advanced to meet him, both hands extended in a pretty gesture of greeting.

"My car broke down." Young Mr. Shelby was explaining, smiling down at Celia, holding both of her hands. "I left it and came on the train."

Celia led him into the living-room. She chattered brightly. She introduced him to Janie and to Hugh.

"I wanted to see you in your own setting." He stood with his back to the fire, taller than Hugh, darker, more finely drawn.

He ought to wear costumes, Janie thought. A brocade vest, a coat with velvet lapels. Strange that his face was dark even when he smiled . . .

Women like a suggestion of mystery, Hugh thought. He doubted if even in the very far South they spoke with such an exaggerated drawl. He thought of the gambler in "Show Boat." Ravenal —that was his name. Celia seemed nervous. He wished he could help her somehow . . .

Carter was better-looking even than she had remembered, Celia thought. He made Hugh look like a college hero. "I wanted to see you in your own setting." Such a shabby setting! Was there a hint of mockery in his smile? . . .

"Have you had lunch?" Celia asked when Hugh

had taken his coat and Janie had pushed the arm-chair close to the fire.

"Well, no. As a matter of fact ———" He accepted a cigarette and bent to the lighter Hugh snapped.

Lunch! Celia thought of Rachel in bed with neuritis. She thought of what was left in the ice-box. She thought of Mother lunching with Mrs. Leland. She felt very badly used.

Janie was sorry for Celia. She couldn't bear it, somehow, to see her shaken and nervous. She wished she had dusted this morning and rearranged the flowers.

"Our maid is ill," she explained to Carter Shelby. "And Mother isn't at home. Last night we killed the fatted calf." She smiled her wide gay smile. "There's nothing left but his bones."

Hugh laughed. Why will she say such things? Celia inwardly fumed. Carter Shelby smiled.

"The prodigal son," he said, "did not depend on a motor . . . Mulberry Square! You described it so beautifully, Celia."

Celia's lips trembled. Janie thought very quickly.

"Why don't you go out to Aunt Lucy's?" she suggested.

"I'll call her." Celia felt almost grateful to Janie.

They heard her talking at the telephone in the hall . . . "If it wouldn't be too much trouble."

The silver harp strings were singing. "Thank you, Aunt Lucy! That's simply darling of you . . ."

She was smiling when she returned to the living room.

"I'll run you out," Hugh offered.

"No, thank you." Celia's smile was not for Hugh. "Aunt Lucy is sending William in with the sedan." She crossed to the foot-stool and sat so that the firelight would shine across her hair. She looked up at Carter Shelby, her delicate face bound in a wimple of gold.

"I'm afraid I exaggerated," she confessed with a rueful smile. "I love the old house so. It seems beautiful to me." The pleased dreamy expression crept into her eyes. "Do you think I am very old-fashioned and a silly quaint little girl?"

Celia was Celia, playing a rôle, weaving romances again.

III

"Hugh." Mother stood in the living-room door. Her expression was worried and anxious.

"Yes, Mrs. Ballard." Hugh looked up from the chess board. Janie halted the victorious march of an ivory knight.

"Celia seems terribly upset." Mother's hand trembled against the dull blue portière. "And the Doctor is out. Will you fix her something to make her sleep?"

A few minutes later Hugh knocked gently at Celia's door.

"Come in," a faint voice called.

Celia lay propped up against a heap of fluffy pillows in the lilac and ivory bed. Her face was wan and wistful. The light from the bedside lamp made a halo above her head. Mother was not in the room. The rain lashed fitfully against the windows. There was in the air a faint haunting fragrance. Lilies-of-the-valley.

"What is it, Celia?" Hugh drew a chair beside the bed.

"I'm utterly wretched." Her lips quivered. Her eyes were misted with tears. "I can't go to sleep."

"Drink this." He lifted her head from the pillows, tingling at the touch of her hair and the petal smoothness of her skin.

She drank the mixture like an obedient child, her misty eyes lifting above the rim of the glass.

"Tell me what happened, Celia?" Hugh settled the pillows behind her head. "You'll feel better if you talk it all out."

"It's just—me." The silver harp strings were muted to threads of sound. "I can't bear to be disappointed in my—my friends."

That Shelby with his mocking eyes! Hugh's hand knotted into a capable fist.

"Tell me, Celia." His voice was unsteady. There was a hammering in his ears. She looked so lovely and helpless and fragile in the nest of fluffy cushions.

"I see only good in people," Celia murmured as though she were talking to herself. "I blow pretty bubbles and when they are pricked ——" Her voice trailed off into silence. A tear slipped slowly between her lashes.

"Don't Celia! Don't cry!"

"Life is so hard." A second tear followed the path of the first. "Sometimes I think I'll go into a convent."

"Celia!"

"It would be heavenly, Hugh." She wore her "Saint Cecelia" expression. Hugh saw her, lovely, fragile and forever beyond his reach in the somber garb of a nun. "No more hurts and disappointments. Just nothing but silence and praying and peace."

"My lovely Celia!"

"You do understand me, Hugh?" Celia returned from the convent. She smiled faintly, a poignant smile, misted over with tears. "You don't think I'm just an over-sensitive little goose?"

Her hand lay like a porcelain flower against the spread of lilac silk. Hugh stooped quickly, brushed it with his cheek.

"Celia," he said brokenly. "Celia!"

VIII

I

THE White Marsh creek wound its twisting course through stretches of yellow-green reeds. The sun made a sheen on the water; the sky was a clear lovely blue. Janie pulled occasionally on the oars to keep the boat in the current. In between times she sat very still and thought of many things. This was her last day at home.

Father was fishing. He sat in the stern of the boat and patiently trolled a line. It was a labor of love. There were, apparently, no fish left in all of the winding creek. Father didn't seem to mind. He puffed on his pipe and watched the lazy ripples. When he glanced at Janie, his eyes, under the brim of a battered felt hat, were tranquil and content. He looked brown and healthy in his flannel shirt and his corduroy trousers. Dear Father! Janie's heart swelled with tender affection. She could feel it, pressing against her chest, knotting a lump in her throat.

There was always a lump in her throat. She was glad she was going away. It hurt it more than she

could bear to watch Hugh fall in love with Celia.
He still went swimming with Janie and teased her
and called her "a good little egg."   But it wasn't
quite the same.   He was moody and thoughtful.
His eyes, when he glanced at Celia, had a new sort
of worshipping look.   It had happened —— Janie
thought back through the past two weeks.   It had
happened, she decided, just after Carter Shelby had
come and gone.

It was strange about that visit.   The postman
brought no more square gray envelopes.   Mother
dreamed no longer over the picture of a rose brick
mansion—"*Magnolia*—Home of Colonel Valentine
Shelby."   The volume of "Centuries" which en-
tombed that dazzling vision, stood with the others,
collecting dust in the shelves of the upstairs book-
case.

Celia refused to discuss the matter.   In answer
to Mother's questions she merely said, "When il-
lusions are shattered, there is nothing left."   Then
she looked very lovely and sad and too fragile to
endure the disappointments of life.   Mother and
Great-aunt Rose believed that Celia had dismissed
Carter Shelby because he had failed to measure up
to her high ideals.   It brightened Celia's halo.   It
shed a radiance about her.   It made Janie a little
sick . . .

"Look out there, Skipper!"

Janie roused with a start.   The boat had nosed

itself into the rushes; the oars were tangled in
clumps of reeds.

"I'm sorry, Father. I was thinking."

"This is a good place to stop." Father tapped
the bowl of his pipe against the seat. He tucked it
into his pocket. He pulled in his trailing line.
"Let's see what Rachel packed in the basket. I
have an appetite these days."

There were sandwiches in the basket and peaches
and cookies stuffed with figs. Janie sat in the bot-
tom of the boat, hugging her knees in her arms,
leaning her head against Father's knee.

"Mother was cross at us," Father said, "for running away to-day." He chuckled gleefully, like a
boy playing hooky from school. That was one of
Father's charms. He had never entirely grown up.

"She thought I ought to help her pack my trunks."
. . . She was going away! It would be three
months until the Christmas vacation. Three
months and three hundred miles stretching between
Janie and Mulberry Square. Perhaps, then, she
wouldn't mind so much. Ninety days. Hugh had
marked them on the calendar in the office.
Hugh . . .

"I'll miss you, little fellow."

Little Fellow! Hugh called her that. He called
Celia "darling." She had heard him in the garden
one night. Darling! Darling! Darling! . . .

"I'll miss *you*, Father," she said.

"You aren't really eating, Janie. You're nibbling like a mouse."

"I—I'm not very hungry."

"Aren't you feeling well?"

"I have a lump in my throat."

"Tell me . . . Can you, Baby?"

She could always tell Father. As far back as she could remember, she could always tell Father about the things that hurt. Only this time it was different . . .

"It's going away, I guess."

"We'll do something pleasant to-night."

"I have an engagement with Hugh."

"Engagement?" Father's voice was amused. "Is it something very important?"

"He asked me to have supper with him at the Inn because it's my last night at home. We'll dance for a little while" . . . Dancing with Hugh. There would be a moon. It was waiting now in the sky, misty, unnoticed, a thin white ghost of a moon . . .

"I'm proud of Hugh," Father said warmly. "Between us we're doing a pretty good job."

Janie nodded . . . "I couldn't have stayed if you hadn't been here to scold me and take me swimming." Hugh . . . !

They were silent for a moment. The reeds all around them rustled with a gentle slurring sound, like the rustle of the taffeta skirts that Mother used to wear . . . "Janie is such a plain little thing." "Curtsey to Aunt Rose, dear. See—like Celia does." "Celia is a sweet-tempered child. Sing your French song, Celia." Celia! Celia! Celia! Celia! . . . "Darling, darling, darling," sang the Chinese nightingale. Only it wasn't a nightingale. It was Hugh, talking to Celia in the garden . . .

"Next June," Father presently said, "you and I are going to take a trip."

"Where?" she asked, not caring very much.

"A fishing trip to Canada." Father's voice was excited and pleased. "Jumping Trout lake. I haven't been there for more than twenty years."

"Is it pretty?" She wanted to be interested in Father's lake. But she wasn't, really. She kept hearing the Chinese nightingale. Only it wasn't a nightingale. It was Hugh, talking to Celia in the garden . . .

Father told her about the lake, silver and smooth, with the forest all around. There were mountains, he said, the Laurentian mountains, smoky and blue. The trout were speckled in rainbow colors. You cast for them with a fly. The forest had a lovely smell, cedars and hemlocks and pines.

Pines! There were pines at the tip of the point, craggly pines with ragged plumes. There was a wintergreen smell and small soft chirpings of birds . . .

"Look at our Christmas tree now!"

"You can't see the tiny first star."

"It's lost in the dazzle" . . .

"Janie! You're crying, Janie."

"No—no, I'm not."

"There's a tear on your knee."

She saw it, catching the sunlight, a small round tear on her bare brown knee.

"What a funny place for a tear!" She tried very hard to smile.

"Janie——" Father's voice was very gentle. "Are you unhappy, dear?"

She nodded.

"Why?"

She couldn't tell him why. It was like being happy, mixed up with so many things; being glad to go away, not caring about Father's lake, Hugh falling in love with Celia, her little brown dog that had died so long ago. His hair was brown like the cat o' nine tails growing among the reeds. A dear little dog. Celia had let him be killed. Hugh was in love with Celia. "Darling, darling, darling, sang the Chinese nightingale" . . .

"I just feel sad," she said.

"You care so about things, Janie."

"I wish I didn't." She looked up at him with troubled young eyes. "Can you help it, Father, if that's the way you are made?"

"You can't help it, dear." Father was stroking her hair. She could feel his fingers, gentle, caressing, firm. "It isn't a bad way to be. You are hurt more often but you enjoy everything more. Remember, Janie, if you couldn't feel very unhappy, you could never feel very happy. Do you understand?"

"Yes, Father."

"It isn't the most comfortable way to live," Father continued. "But it makes you more of a person."

"Do you remember," Janie asked, "how Grandmother Ballard used to say, 'Consider the stars, my dear'?"

"That's a philosophy for grandmothers," Father said. "It doesn't work with brown little gypsy girls."

He talked to her, then, about being brave and learning something from all the hurts. It was sad and very beautiful. The reeds rustled softly. Father stroked her hair. A bird flew low above their heads, a bird with a speckled brown breast. Months later, Janie remembered the rustling sound of the reeds, the bird with the speckled brown breast. She scarcely noticed them now. She kept seeing Hugh with that worshipping look in his eyes.

She wanted to feel how much she loved Father, how happy she would be to camp with him on the shore of his silver lake. But she couldn't, somehow. A thin white moon was waiting up there in the shining blue of the sky. She kept thinking of dancing with Hugh. Her heart grew larger and larger. There was an aching in her wrists. All of her was racing forward toward the evening. She

didn't want to race away from Father. It was
something she couldn't help.

Suddenly guilty, she pressed her cheek against his
knee.

"Why, Janie!"

"I love you, Father," she said.

II

Janie dressed with the greatest care. Filmy un-
derthings, chiffon stockings, garters with wee pink
roses. Her fingers trembled as she tied the butterfly bows on the creamy kid slippers that Hugh had
bought. There was going to be a moon . . .

She brushed her hair until it shone. How brown
she was! Mother was right. She did look like a
gypsy. If only she could be as pretty as Celia!
Just for to-night. Father said she was prettier inside. If only just for to-night she could wear herself
inside out!

The creamy dress from Paris. She popped her
head through the neckline and fastened the tiny
loops. It was a beautiful dress. She thought she
looked rather nice. Perhaps she could borrow
Celia's shawl with the silky golden fringe. Aunt
Rose gave it to Celia for Christmas. Aunt Rose
gave Janie a fountain pen. Aunt Rose's presents
were always like that.

Celia was not in her room. Janie wondered idly
where Celia had gone. She thought she would use

a little perfume, a drop on the lobe of each ear.
There was a new bottle on Celia's dressing table.
Lilies-of-the-Valley . . . "That's how I thought of
you," Hugh had said, "Lilies-of-the-valley." . . .
Janie pushed in the stopper. She wouldn't touch it,
not even a single drop.

Where did Celia keep her shawl? Janie crossed
to the wardrobe. A letter was lying on the floor
beside the cream and ivory desk. Janie recognized
Muriel's writing. It was strange, she thought, that
Muriel had written to Celia so soon. She and
Aunt Lucy had returned to Washington only a few
days ago. She picked up the letter. A sentence
caught her attention . . . "Carter Shelby had dinner with us last night" . . . There was a mark on
the paper, the mark of a small French heel. It
must have been an angry heel which stamped with
a great deal of force. Even the nail prints showed.

The shawl was not in the wardrobe. Janie decided not to rummage around. She could ask Celia
just as well. The cream and lilac room disturbed
her. It seemed to be filled with Celia's poses.

Celia was not downstairs. Janie questioned
Mother.

"She went out about three o'clock." Mother was
setting the table. "Why are you wearing that
dress?"

"Hugh asked me to have supper with him."
Janie spoke the words slowly. It made them seem
more real. "Just set the table for three."

"You won't be out late?"

"No, Mother."

"Be home by ten, dear. You'll have to make an early start in the morning."

To-morrow? There was no to-morrow. There was only a moon and to-night . . .

The clock on the landing struck six. Hugh had not come in. Celia had not returned. Janie wandered through the hall, through the living-room, out on the porch and back again to the hall. Father came down the stairs.

"Hasn't Hugh come in yet?" he asked.

Janie shook her head.

Mother came out from the dining-room.

"John," she said. "I'm worried about Celia."

Father was familiar with Mother's worrying habit.

"She's out on Manor street," he said easily, "or at Rhoda's, perhaps."

"It isn't like her not to tell me," Mother fretted. "She knows how I worry."

"You can worry while you're eating, can't you?" Father asked with a smile. "It's one of my accomplishments."

"You'd better eat something, Janie." Mother moved uncertainly toward the dining-room door. "Goodness knows ——"

"I'm having supper with Hugh." Saying the words aloud reassured her. She heard less distinctly the clamor of fear in her heart.

Through the hall, through the living-room, out on the porch, back again to the hall. The clock on the landing struck seven. Were they together, Celia and Hugh? A grave little face in the mirror above the card tray table. The blur of a creamy frock in the slowly gathering shadows. Small kid slippers with butterfly bows pacing a dreary round. Through the hall, through the living-room . . .

"I am simply distracted." Mother was talking at the 'phone. "I've called everybody . . . Hugh isn't here either . . . Well, I *had* thought of that" . . .

Janie had thought of it, too. Hugh and Celia. Mother was pleased. Why shouldn't she be? She didn't know that Janie was being hurt. A small grave person, silent and tense, on the Chesterfield in the hall. A frock with a border of flowers stitched in colors around the hem. Small kid slippers that wanted to dance . . .

The fan-light paled from amber to mauve, the gray of twilight to night. Old Thomas came to bid Janie good-bye.

"We'll miss you, Janie." A softened note in the gruff old voice. "The Square's not the same without you."

"I'll miss *you*, Thomas." Two slim brown arms around his neck. A tear on his rough woolen coat. "Take care of your rheumatism. I'll see you at Christmas time."

Mother talked at the telephone . . . "I'm at the

end of my wits . . . It isn't like Celia . . . Hugh isn't here, either" . . .

Hugh with his tumbled bright hair and his laughing ruddy-brown eyes. "Five feet tall, rather small" . . .

"No thank you, Rachel. I don't want anything to eat."

Miss Ellie came with a present.

"Thank you, Miss Ellie." The gay little laughing notes bravely doing their best. "You made it all by hand."

"It isn't much." A pleased expression. A timid, apologetic cough. "You look so nice in that apricot color."

"John, it's after nine o'clock." Mother expecting the worst.

"I'm going out on Manor street." Father at the door. "You can reach me at Archer's or Leland's. Want to go, Janie?"

"No thank you, Father. I'd rather stay here."

Great-uncle Charlie came with a necklace of amber beads.

"I've been saving them for you, Janie."

"Oh thank you, Uncle Charlie!" The beads all slipping together, a misted blur of color.

"Where can they be?" Mother fretting and fuming, painting horrible pictures.

"Celia and Hugh?"

"Celia and Hugh, Uncle Charlie." A chin that quivered forlornly. A tear that couldn't be checked.

"My sainted Aunt Maria! I wish I was asleep!"

They came as the clock was striking ten. They came like a burst of music in through the wide front door. Celia was radiant. Hugh had a shine in his eyes.

"Where have you been?" Mother cried. "Where in the world have you been?"

"Mother!" Celia flung herself into Mother's arms with a pretty radiant gesture. "Oh, Mother! What do you think?"

"We've been getting engaged," Hugh said in a voice that was solemn and happy and hushed. "That is, if you have no objections."

Janie said nothing at all. She sat on the Chesterfield silent and still, her fingers twisting together.

"Celia darling!" Mother was laughing and crying, too. "Well, Hugh, this is a surprise!"

Janie slipped out into the kitchen. The slippers that had wanted to dance tripped and stumbled climbing the dark back stairs.

III

"Janie . . ."

That was Hugh! Janie, curled up in the window seat of her own small room was breathless and very still. She couldn't talk to Hugh to-night. The happy sound of his voice was more than she could bear.

"I know you are there. I can see a light through the key-hole."

She wished she hadn't lit the candles on the dresser. But it had been unbearably lonesome sitting here in the dark.

"Janie, dear," Hugh was calling. "Have you gone to bed?"

Janie said nothing at all.

"I'm coming in anyway." He opened the door. Janie saw in the candle glow the happy shine in his eyes. She turned her head. She looked down through the window at the misty lights in the Square.

"Why are you sitting up here alone?" he asked with a crinkly smile.

"I—I'm thinking."

"They're making a fuss downstairs." He sat beside her on the window seat. He was obliged to sit very close. "But you weren't there."

"Did you miss me, Hugh?"

"Of course I missed you," he said softly. "I've been searching all over the house. Why did you run away? Aren't you glad I'm to be your brother?"

Janie nodded. In the place where her heart should have been there was nothing at all but an ache.

He told her how happy he was. He said lovely things about Celia. He didn't remember that he had invited her to have supper with him. He didn't think that her slippers had wanted to dance. He didn't know that the moon had been waiting all day to shine for Janie and Hugh. She didn't tell him. She just looked down from the window at the blurred yellow lights in the Square. Hugh was looking down, too.

"Lord," he said in a hushed sort of voice, "the Square is grand to-night. There was moonlight the night I arrived. Do you remember?"

Did she remember? Would she ever forget as long as she lived?

"There was a hurdy-gurdy by the fountain."

Janie heard it again, the wheezy familiar tune . . . "We strolled the lanes together" . . .

"We sat under the mulberry trees," he continued. "I told you a story about a boy named Hugh."

A little boy in a big brown house. A lad in a uniform with his chest puffed out and his eyes staring straight ahead. A red-haired young man with a crinkly smile who understood when she didn't know why she was happy. Janie loved them all. She cared so dreadfully hard.

He talked softly on and on. He did not appear to notice that Janie said nothing at all. He was absorbed in his own great happiness. Janie forgave him. He didn't know she was being hurt. He never, never should know.

"I didn't like it at first," Hugh said presently. "I thought it was pretty dreadful. I never dreamed

I'd find the loveliest thing in life right here in Mulberry Square."

He didn't mean a "good little egg" who had scolded him and taken him swimming and made him toe the mark. He didn't mean a brown little girl named Janie who loved him very much. He was thinking of Celia all creamy and golden, pretty selfish Celia with her look of a porcelain saint . . .

"You're quiet, Janie." He remembered her after a while. "What's the matter, little fellow?"

Little Fellow! If he just wouldn't call her that . . .

"I—I feel sort of sad."

"Why?"

"Leaving, I guess."

"It won't be long until Christmas." He lifted her hand. "Here's something to take with you." He kissed the palm of her hand and folded her fingers over the kiss to keep it from slipping away.

Oh, Hugh! But he didn't know he was hurting her worse than she had ever been hurt in all her life before. Oh, dear big laughing Hugh! . . .

"I want something in exchange." He tilted her chin. "I want your lovely smile."

She had to smile. He was looking at her with eyes that were tender and teasing. She had to smile. There were tears on her lashes and a choking lump in her throat. But somehow, she managed it— her wide gay gorgeous smile.

Hugh pretended to catch the smile and tuck it into the pocket over his heart.

"I'll take it out when it's raining," he said, "and turn it on like a moon."

He took it away with him, Janie's smile in his pocket. He left a kiss in the palm of her small brown hand. He went downstairs to Celia with a swift and hurrying step.

Janie curled down in the window seat among the chintz cushions. She was tired, so dreadfully tired. The candles burned lower and lower. The leaves outside rustled drowsily against the screen. Too tired to think. Too weary for tears. Tired, so dreadfully tired . . .

The moon slanting in through the locust boughs kept a rendezvous with the slippers that wanted to dance. Janie did not know that. She fell asleep with her cheek pressed close against the palm of her hand.

Part Two

XIX

I

THE wheels of the train made a singing sound against the icy rails. The windows were patterned with crystal fern fronds of frost. The car had been chilly all day. Little draughts edged in through the window casings and eddied along the floor. Janie tucked her feet up under the edge of her coat, buried her chin in the soft fur collar and wondered if she would ever again be warm.

It was the inside cold that was hardest to bear, the icy cold of fear. At intervals she napped a little. When a sudden jolt roused her, the cold closed in around her again. Each time it was like living over that first frozen moment again. She had not been able to believe it. The telegram had slipped away from her hand. Midge, her room-mate, had read it, fat little Midge . . . "Father is ill. Come at once" . . . Midge had a cold in her head. It made the words sound queer. Funny to think of a thing like that. Father was ill and all that Janie had thought of was Midge with a cold in her head.

It was hard to believe a thing that never had

happened before. Father had never been ill. In all her life Janie could not remember when Father had ever been ill. A dreadful thing couldn't happen so quickly as this. Two days ago she had received a letter from Father, a jolly letter, full of plans for Christmas when Janie would be at home. Now she was going home, a day ahead of time. Midge had read the message . . . "Father is ill. Come at once" . . .

They had all been so kind to Janie, the teachers, the Dean, the girls. They had sent a telegram home. They had bought her tickets and packed her trunks. Midge had sniffled and sobbed until her face was as red as a ripe tomato. Janie hadn't cried. She had just sat still and tried to drink the cocoa Miss Eldridge brought. She wanted to cry. But it didn't seem real. She couldn't believe that it was Janie's trunk they were packing, that Janie's father was ill.

She couldn't believe it now. The telegram was in her pocket-book. She unfolded the creased yellow sheet and read the message again. Hugh had sent it. Hugh! She tried to see Hugh in her mind; his copper-gold head, his wide laughing mouth, his eyes that were the color of sherry wine. They were only words. They didn't make for her a life-like picture of Hugh. She had always been able to see him. During those first weeks at college, she had seen him everywhere. Now, when she tried so hard, she couldn't see him at all.

She looked at her hand where Hugh had kissed it that last lonely night at home. It was just Janie's hand, the pink of the palm traced with faint uneven lines. If she could remember how she had felt that night maybe then she could cry. She remembered the candle-light and the pattern of the chintz on the window-seat cushions. She remembered the smell of Hugh's coat, tobacco and tweed mixed with the doctor smell of antiseptics and drugs. She remembered unimportant things; the leaves brushing against the screen, voices in the Square, the bows on her slippers, the blue-bells and yellow roses stitched in a careless border around the hem of her frock. But she couldn't remember how she had felt. She couldn't cry or make it seem real that Janie's father was ill . . .

"Some storm, eh George?" The man ahead of her said.

"Yessuh!" The colored porter was grinning from ear to ear. "White Chrismus make a lean grave-yahd. Reckon we-all gwine to cheat de debbil dis yeah."

Christmas! They had made such beautiful plans. Hugh had written to her about it and Father and Mother and Celia. At first she had dreaded going back home. But the worst of the feeling had gone. Celia seemed to be happy, being engaged to Hugh. She wrote Janie affectionate letters. Because she was human and not a saint, Janie couldn't exactly rejoice. But she could not mind quite so much if

Celia loved Hugh and both of them were happy.
She had been, at the last, almost anxious for Christmas to come. There were boxes in her trunk tied
with silver and scarlet ribbons. She couldn't feel
miserable all the time when Christmas was in the
air. And now she was going home. She didn't feel
happy or miserable or anything at all. She was
frozen like ice inside . . .

The train rushed on through the early twilight.
The globes in the ceiling filled the car with a dim
flickering light. Shadows trooped with the eddying
gusts along the narrow aisle. Station lights bloomed
and faded through the frosted window panes.

"Will we make Philadelphia on schedule,
George?" asked the man ahead of Janie.

"Fifty minutes late, suh. Can't make no time in
a blizza'd."

"Will the branch trains wait?" Janie asked. Her
voice sounded strange. It was the first time she
had spoken all day.

"Where to, Miss?"

"New Kingston." New Kingston! Why that
was home . . .

"Reckon so."

Janie scarcely heard the words. If the branch
train shouldn't wait! She looked at her watch. She
prayed little soundless prayers. The train seemed
not to be moving at all. An endless eternity passed.
The station lights bloomed more thickly now. People in the car made a stir of reaching for luggage

and buttoning coats. Janie pulled on her green cap
edged with beaver, fastened the beaver collar of
her new green coat, buckled her galoshes and then
sat very still.

The train ran slowly in under the tunnel of shed.
Janie moved with the stream of passengers toward
the door. She felt the wind nipping her cheeks and
her fingertips. A red-cap had her bag. She was
following him through the crowded station.

"New Kingston, Miss?"

"Has it gone? Oh please, has it gone?"

"Waitin' fo' the Express."

Oh, thank you God or the P.R.R. or whoever
makes branch trains wait! A quarter for the porter.
People pushing. Icy steps. A hand helping her up.

"Well, Janie!"

She looked up into a familiar face. It was Mr.
Mapes the conductor who lived in New Kingston.
Mr. Mapes was not handsome. He had a cadaver-
ous face and bushy brows and hair sprouting out
of his ears. To Janie he looked beautiful. He
was a familiar friend.

"Father?" she asked.

"He's holding on."

"How? When?"

"Accident. It happened early last night in the
storm."

The sound of a familiar voice after the long
weary journey alone broke the ice around Janie's
heart. She clung to the friendly conductor, pressed

her face against his buttons, sobbed gratefully in his arms.

"There, there, Janie." He led her into the car. "We're ready to go. In half an hour we'll have you safe at home."

Mr. Mapes jerked a handkerchief out of his pocket and solemnly blew his nose.

II

Hugh was waiting on the platform. Janie saw his face, raised to watch the windows as the train moved past. Her heart turned over. She knew that he would be sorry, of course. She had not expected to find him so haggard and white and distressed. He saw her and lifted his hand. His eyes, beneath the down-turned brim of his hat, brightened for a moment and then were somber again.

"Hugh! Oh here I am, Hugh!" She tumbled down the train steps straight into his arms.

"Janie! Thank God you are here!"

Horatius was parked in the station drive, chugging sturdily, covered all over with snow.

"Tuck the rug in, Janie."

"I'm all right. Tell me about it, Hugh."

"He crashed into a gully beyond the White Marsh creek." They were moving now. Horatius was ploughing through the snow.

"Was he alone?"

"Yes." Hugh's voice was rough and husky. "He

was coming home from the Weaver place. There's another baby out there."

"Is—is he terribly hurt?"

Hugh did not answer. Icy fingers clutched Janie's heart. She glanced up at him swiftly. A dim light filtered in from the street through the ising-glass squares in the curtains. She could see that his face was haunted and white.

"Tell me, Hugh." She clutched at his arm. "I have to know. Is he ——" The word stuck tight in her throat.

"He's still unconscious. They don't know yet." Hugh repeated the words dully as though he had said them a great many times. "He's at the hospital."

"Can I see him to-night?"

"Not to-night, little fellow. To-morrow, perhaps."

He told her, in words which Janie could understand, what Father's condition might be. She couldn't believe, somehow, that he was talking about Father. She had heard Father and Hugh discuss cases like that dozens and dozens of times. It couldn't be Father. Why, Market street was strung with lights as it always was at Christmas. And there was Leland's window of toys with the mechanical clown bobbing his head as he had for years and years. There were Christmas trees on the corners bound together like wigwams and holly wreaths tilting in heaps. Everything was just as it always had been. This dreadful thing couldn't be true . . .

"God wouldn't let Father die," she said with a sort of confidence. "He's always been so kind and so good. God couldn't let Father die."

"Do you believe that, Janie?" Hugh asked brokenly.

"I—I'm trying to."

"Keep on," he said, "and make me believe it, too."

The Square was a wilderness of wind and swirling snow. The arc-lights shone faintly. The lights in the houses were misted blurs of yellow and pink. The mulberry trees were dim white mounds . . . "There were four mulberry trees" . . .That was a very long time ago . . .

"It all seems so—so usual," Janie said. "Just as it's always been." She couldn't think of the Square without Father. What would people do?

The car drew up at the curb in front of the old brick house. The downstairs windows were lighted. The fan-light was a yellow crescent. The lanterns were twinkling. It was home.

Hugh lifted her out of the car, held her for a moment before he set her down on her feet.

"I'm glad you're here, little fellow." Her cheek brushed his. His cheek was wet. It might be the melting snow.

"Oh, Hugh!"

The front door opened. A wave of light washed down the snowy steps.

"Janie!" Celia was clinging to Janie as though she would never let go, Celia who was three years older than Janie and taller by three full inches. "Oh, Janie, I'm glad you're home."

Celia was pale. There were shadows under her eyes. Janie was sure that Celia hadn't noticed they were becoming. It made her love Celia as she had loved her once a very long time ago. The flash of the ring on her slender left hand was hard, for a moment, to bear. After that she didn't mind —at least, not so much.

"Where's Mother?" It all looked so usual; the polished stairs, the Chesterfield, the painting in the hall. Surely in just a moment Father would come out from the office, smiling, calling to her, holding out both of his arms . . .

"Mother is staying at the hospital." There was a sweetness about Celia. She had never looked so lovely. "I'm taking her out some things."

"Can't I go?" Janie asked.

"You couldn't see Father." Celia's eyes brimmed over with tears. "And you must be tired. Take care of her, Hugh. Stoney will drive me out."

There was Stoney waiting at the end of the hall, a dumb look of anguish in his eyes.

" 'Evenin', Miss Janie."

"Hello, Stoney." She wanted to do something for Stoney. His eyes were like the eyes of a dog whose master has gone. She could only press his hand and hope that, somehow, it would help.

Rachel, suspiciously red around the eyes, lumbered out into the hall.

"Ain't none of you got no gumption," she scolded, "lettin' dis chile stan' aroun' in soakin' wet wraps?"

"Rachel!" Janie's arms were around her neck. She was clinging hard to something that was familiar and solid and dear.

"Go on wid you!" Rachel was wiping her eyes on her apron. "I'm fixin' you a bite of somethin' to eat." She lumbered back toward the kitchen, grumbling.

It was Hugh who removed Janie's coat and set her on the Chesterfield to unbuckle her galoshes. Celia picked them up to put them away in the closet.

"They're so tiny," she said. "I never remember that Janie is so small."

"Small," Hugh added, "and nice. She's a very good little egg."

III

Janie lay on the living-room davenport pulled close to the crackling fire. Hugh sat on a foot-stool and fed her things from a tray.

"Open your mouth, small person."

"I don't want anything else."

"One more bite. We can't have you getting sick."

She swallowed the bite obediently. In spite of everything, it was lovely to be at home.

"I'm getting warm." She snuggled into the cushions. "I've been so cold all day."

"Poor baby!" Hugh held her hand in both of his. "It's my fault, Janie," he said.

"What is, Hugh?"

"All—all this."

"You mean—Father?"

He nodded his head.

"Why is it your fault, Hugh?"

"It was my patient." His voice was rough and husky. "I knew that baby was coming. I had been there at noon."

"Where were you?"

"I'm ashamed to tell you." He stared miserably at the fire. Janie could feel that his hands were shaking.

"Please, Hugh. Tell me, please."

"I was at the movies. They called twice. Then Doctor Ballard went."

"Oh, Hugh!" The gentle reproach in her husky voice cut like a knife.

"I was, Janie," he repeated dully. "I was sitting in the movies. Doctor Ballard went out to do my job. He hadn't expected to go out at all last night. He had given Stoney the evening off. It had begun to storm. You know he doesn't see well enough to drive at night."

"Oh, Hugh!" She could only say it over and over, that husky reproachful "Oh, Hugh!"

"I'd have done anything for him." Hugh dropped his head on the edge of the davenport over her hand and his own. She felt a wetness on his cheeks. There was no snow in here. "He's been like a father to me. It's my fault, Janie. I can see well enough to drive at night. I shouldn't have let her ——" he stopped abruptly.

Janie was, all at once, breathless and very still.

"It wasn't her fault," Hugh said quickly. "I shouldn't have let her ——"

"She coaxed you to take her?" Janie asked evenly. Oh, Celia! Celia!

"I have been busy." Hugh framed a defense for Celia. "I haven't had time to take her places. She's been sweet about it. I'm horribly jealous, Janie."

"She said she would go with somebody else?"

Hugh had left the foot-stool and was pacing back and forth across the hearth.

"She might." His hands were knotted into fists. "Sometime, she might. I was thinking of that. I—I took her to the movies."

Janie wanted to comfort him. It hurt her to see him so miserable. If only she knew what to say . . .

"Come here, Hugh."

He crossed to the davenport.

"Sit down. I can't talk to you when you're way up there."

"Do you want to talk to me, Janie?" He was sitting beside her again. "I should think you would despise me."

Despise him? You loved the people you loved no matter what they did. You were sorry and hurt but you loved them just the same. Janie couldn't quite reason it out. She knew only that, in the case of Janie, it was true.

"Hugh," she said very gravely, "you mustn't take all this blame. It might have happened some other way. It might ——"

"But it happened *this* way." Hugh's eyes were young and tragic. "I swear to you, Janie, I'll do anything to make up for it—anything in the world."

The vein in his forehead was throbbing. It always throbbed when he was angry or very much in earnest. It was Hugh's barometer. Stormy weather when the vein in his forehead throbbed. Her eyes traveled slowly over his face. The old laughing Hugh was gone. She wanted him to come back. She wondered if ever he would.

"Things happen," she said. "We can't help them. We can only try to be brave."

"Janie!" He dropped his head into the hollow of her arm. He looked tired and very young with the firelight glinting across his hair and his chin so stubbornly set.

"I talk like a lady reformer." Janie was laughing and crying, too.

"You're a comfortable small person," Hugh said wearily. "I'm glad you've come back to the Square."

Janie drew a quivering sigh. She felt entirely grown up.

IV

"Janie!"

"What is it?" Janie, her heart in her mouth, switched on the light beside Mother's bed. Celia, huddled in a bath-robe, was closing the door behind her.

"Have they 'phoned from the hospital?" Janie asked.

"No." Celia's teeth were chattering with the cold. "I was frightened. Can I sleep in here with you?"

Janie snapped off the light. They lay curled together in the middle of the wide soft bed.

"It wasn't my fault, was it, Janie?" Celia presently asked.

"I don't know."

"Janie, please say that it wasn't." Celia was trembling all over. "It might have happened anyway. Please say that it wasn't my fault."

Janie only once before had ever seen Celia so frantic and shaken with fear. That was when she had pushed Janie one day when they were playing in the Square. Janie had fallen. Her head had bumped against the fountain. She had lain there dreadfully still. She remembered that as she had opened her eyes Celia was sobbing, "It wasn't my fault, was it? Please say that it wasn't my fault."

"I don't know," she repeated, puzzled about it all.

"How could I know?" Celia was close to hysterics. "I love Father dearly. Hugh is absurd. It wasn't his fault or mine."

"Don't think about it now," Janie said gently. "Father wouldn't want you to be unhappy."

"I'll be nicer," Celia promised, "if God will let Father get well."

She had promised that years ago when Janie lay beside the fountain so dreadfully white and still. She hadn't remembered very long. She had told people Janie slipped.

"If you'd only say that it wasn't my fault," Celia was trembling and shaking with sobs. "If you'd only tell me, Janie."

Janie couldn't say that. She couldn't scold her either. Celia was trembling so. She put her arms around her instead and nestled very close. They cried in the soft wide bed. Towards morning they slept, curled together, Celia's cheek against Janie's, the brown head and the golden head nestled into the same warm hollow of pillows.

II

I

THERE were anxious days in the old brick house. Father rallied, at times, only to sink back into unconsciousness again. Mother stayed on at the hospital. She had a small room next to Father's with a communicating door. They sat there, sometimes, in the afternoon, Mother and Celia and Janie, holding each other's hands, waiting, talking in whispers, listening for sounds beyond the closed white door.

"We're doing everything possible," Doctor Alden, the Chief-of-Staff, would say. "We can't tell yet."

There were two strange doctors who came at intervals; a round, jolly one with thick white hair, a tall, solemn one with a VanDyke beard.

"We're doing everything possible," they would say. "We can't tell yet."

Once the door opened and Janie saw Father. He looked very long and thin in the narrow white bed. His eyes were closed under white wrappings of bandages. His hand was lying on the counterpane, thin and brown and familiar. Janie remembered

how he had stroked her hair that day on the White
Marsh creek. She heard again the rustling sound
of the reeds, saw the bird with the speckled brown
breast. That day she had run away from Father.
She had been thinking only of Hugh. If they might
go fishing again . . .

Doctor Alden sent them out for drives in his
car. Father's car could never be used again. Hugh
ploughed grimly around in Horatius, trying to do
all of Father's work. Stoney drove Doctor Alden's
big closed car. Mother and Celia and Janie would
sit together on the back seat. Downtown was gay
with Christmas decorations. There were holly
wreaths in the windows along Manor street. The
signs of Christmas, the stir and the bustle, were
more than they could bear. Stoney would drive
them out along the country roads which were clear
enough for travelling. They talked of other
Christmases.

"Do you remember when Father made the fire
burn too high and everything in our stockings
melted?"

"Remember when Celia wanted a pink teddy-bear
and Father searched all over Philadelphia and then,
at the last minute, Mother had to dye a white one
pink?"

"Remember the Christmas eve Father was snow-
bound in the country and Janie wouldn't look at her
presents until he came at noon on Christmas day?"

Remember? Remember? . . .

Mother often rebelled.

"To think of Father being sacrificed for a Weaver baby," she would say with tears in her pretty blue eyes. "They have more now than they can feed."

Mother didn't blame Celia or Hugh. She blamed Father's passion for service. Sometimes there was a hint of fear in the high lovely blue of her eyes.

"If anything *should* happen to Father," she would say. Janie knew she was thinking of money. There was never more than just enough. As Mother often remarked, people thought of Father first in times of distress and last when they paid their bills. There were more unpaid accounts than even Mother suspected in Father's untidy ledger. Janie knew. It seemed unimportant now.

"We'd get along," she would say, thinking only of a world without Father in it anywhere.

"Celia will be taken care of, anyway." Mother would glance gratefully at the ring on Celia's left hand. "Janie and I could manage, I suppose."

Mrs. Quillen, stout and good-natured and anxious to help, was installed in the old brick house. Rachel, grumbling constantly, prepared delicious meals which returned to the kitchen almost untouched. Meals were an ordeal. Three of them, Celia and Janie and Hugh, at the long dining-room table. Mrs. Quillen would not eat with them. She "snacked," as she called it, at odd times in the kitchen. Celia sat at Mother's place and poured the coffee or tea. Father's vacant chair was more than Janie could stand.

"You sit there, Hugh," she suggested one evening at supper.

"I couldn't, Janie." His face was working queerly.

"Father would like it."

"Do you think so?" he asked eagerly.

"I'm sure of it."

Hugh seated himself in the vacant chair. He looked, Janie thought, as though a General had pinned a ribbon on his chest and kissed him on both of his cheeks.

A shadow lay across the Square. People knocked at the kitchen door, shabby people with unashamed tears in their eyes; Tony Silver, the "General" with his wooden leg, girls from the mill, the frowsy citizens of Vine and Juniper streets.

"How's the Doctor this morning?"

"They're doing everything possible. They can't tell yet."

The Square, proper, called at the front door; old Thomas, Miss Ellie with moulds of gelatine and bowls of very weak broth, the mother of the twins with the clothes basket on a sled, the rector and Mrs. Warden. The rector cleared his throat very often and quoted things from the Bible . . . "Greater love hath no man" . . . It belonged in church, Janie thought, or cut in a marble tombstone.

It had nothing to do with Father who had been last summer so healthy and happy and brown.

All day there was a stream of callers. From up-town and downtown, from Manor street and the mill section, people came to inquire for Father. Celia, very pale and lovely in demure little gray wool frocks, answered questions, smiled faintly, led the callers in and out of the living-room. Celia was wonderful, Janie thought. She wished she herself could talk and smile. She couldn't. There was always a lump in her throat.

Aunt Lucy came, unexpectedly, with Muriel and Uncle Frank.

"I was so anxious," she said. Aunt Lucy's face, framed in an astrakan collar, looked very anxious indeed. "We're going to open 'Sportsman's Hall' and stay until after the New Year, at least."

"Anything I can do to help?" Uncle Frank said.

"I'll be in and out every day." Muriel hugged both Janie and Celia . . . Celia and Janie and Muriel playing house in the Square. That was a long time ago . . .

So the days crept on toward Christmas eve. There was no bustle of preparations in the old brick house this year. There was waiting and anxiety, a new quick fear whenever the telephone rang. Father's condition changed very little from day to day.

"We're doing everything possible," the jolly round doctor said.

"We can't tell yet," said the solemn one with the beard.

Janie and Celia clung to each other. Mrs. Quillen swept and dusted and polished. Rachel grumbled and baked and broiled. Stoney kept the furnace roaring and cut enough firewood to last for a couple of years. Uncle Charlie sat with them through the twilights which were hardest of all to bear. He told them stories and made them forget for a little while. There were many ways of expressing sympathy, Janie thought; dusting and biscuits and firewood and jokes.

Hugh worked on with a dogged sort of persistence. He slept in Father's room because there was a telephone on the table beside the bed. Sometimes Janie heard him getting up in the middle of the night. Once she wanted to make him some coffee because it was very cold. She pulled on her bathrobe and slippers and started down the stairs.

Celia was making coffee for Hugh. The electric percolator stood on the card table by the living-room fire. There was no light in the room except the rosy glow of the flames. Celia, in her quilted blue kimono with her hair in silky skeins, was making coffee for Hugh. Janie saw Hugh kiss Celia's wrist as she handed him the cup.

"You're lovely, Celia," he said.

Janie clung to the banister rail. She felt better

after a moment. She slipped back upstairs and crawled into bed.

II

It was seven o'clock on Christmas eve when Doctor Alden opened the door. Janie remembered the time. A messenger boy had just brought a basket of poinsettas and Janie had glanced at the tall clock in the hall. Doctor Alden's face was shining; his eyes were moist. Mother stopped rocking back and forth. Celia's hands crept up to her heart. Janie stood very still with the basket of scarlet flowers. They all looked at Doctor Alden.

"Merry Christmas," he said and blew his nose very loudly.

"You mean——?" Mother's eyes asked the question her lips were unable to frame.

"We're not out of the woods by any means." Doctor Alden had closed the door into Father's room. "But he's conscious and asking for you. You can see him for a moment."

Mother gave a happy cry. Celia flung herself at Doctor Alden and kissed his gray mustache. Janie just stood still with the basket of poinsettas.

"Can I go in first?" she asked. Her grave little face was pale above the scarlet flowers.

Mother murmured. Celia made a low sound of protest. Doctor Alden nodded and blew his nose again.

Father's room was dim and full of shadows. The nurse moved to a window and stood looking out. There were flowers everywhere and Father's head on the pillow in a dim circle of light. He was pale and woefully thin but the eyes under the bandages were Father's eyes. They looked at her and smiled.

"Merry Christmas, Janie," Father's dear voice said.

The scarlet flowers scattered themselves across the floor. Janie's feet had wings. In a moment she was beside the bed with her cheek against Father's hand.

"Father, oh Father!" was all she could say.

"You look like a Christmas candle." Father tilted her chin.

"I'm happy." Her eyes were shining; her lashes were jeweled with tears.

"I'll be home pretty soon." Father's voice was pitifully weak.

"We'll go to Canada next June." She had to make it up to him for running away in her thoughts that afternoon on the creek.

"Jumping Trout Lake." Father's eyes brightened. "You and I, Janie. It's a date."

They were quiet after that. Janie had no words to express the singing in her heart. Father understood. His hand was stroking her hair. She could feel his fingers, gentle, caressing, but very weak.

Janie felt a holy sort of happiness. The chimes were ringing for Christmas . . .

"Look here, young lady." Doctor Alden opened the door. "Somebody else wants a chance."

"Good-night, Father," she kissed his cheek.

"Good-night, baby." He smiled. "A happy Christmas."

"It will be, Father . . . Good-night."

She couldn't go back into Mother's room. She wanted to be alone.

The corridor was dim and quiet. The sill of the window was wide and deep. Janie curled herself up in a ball with her cheek against the pane. The sky was sprinkled with frosty stars. The windows of the Catholic church made splashes of color across the snow. The bells were chiming for Christmas. Life was lovely. The world was a beautiful place.

"Thank you, God," she whispered from the depths of a grateful heart.

III

They stood on the hospital steps, Celia and Janie and Hugh, with a radiance about them. Celia wore an uplifted expression. Hugh's eyes had lost their haunted look. Janie shone like a candle lighted for Christmas eve.

The windows of the Catholic church made splashes of color on the snow.

"Let's go in," Janie suggested. She glanced up at them quickly to see if they were smiling.

They weren't smiling. They walked across the street to the church.

It was dim and quiet inside. There were candles on the altar, tall white candles tipped with jets of yellow flame. There was an odor of incense, a faint fragrance of flowers. People, here and there, were kneeling in the shadowy pews, whispering prayers, slipping their rosary beads.

They walked up the narrow aisle, Celia and Janie and Hugh, with a radiance about them. They entered a pew at the front and knelt facing the altar. Above them the chimes were ringing for Christmas.

Hugh thought of Doctor Ballard's words, "It's all right, my boy. I understand." He thought of how he would try to deserve the Doctor's confidence. Nothing mattered so much as that. What was Celia thinking as she knelt there beside him, her face lifted to the flickering candle flames? Would he ever be permitted to share her thoughts? She eluded him, somehow. Her loveliness was a will-o-the-wisp. Was he too clumsy to capture it? She nestled close against him. He breathed the fragrance of her hair. There was a hammering in his ears. He loved her, he loved her so much . . .

Celia was thinking of Father. She was glad, so glad he was better. That proved that it wasn't her fault. She saw the blue-robed saint in a niche near the altar. The gaudy colors were softened by the candle-light. The saint in her gilded niche reminded her of a painting she once had seen. When Hugh took her abroad she would see the paintings of Botticelli. That funny old man at the mountains last year said she looked like a Botticelli madonna. She felt Hugh's eyes fixed upon her. Was he thinking that she looked like the blue-robed saint in the gilded niche? She moved a little closer to him. She felt that he was trembling. How terribly he loved her. More than she loved him. Her lips curved in a remote ethereal smile. She wore her "Saint Cecelia" expression.

Janie was filled with a happiness too high and too holy for thought. Her hazel eyes lifted to the candles on the altar were brighter than the jets of golden flame. Her grave little face was entirely unconscious of the exalted expression it wore. The happiness was a pain. It hurt her even to breathe. Her heart grew larger and larger. She had to share it with somebody. She glanced shyly up at Hugh, wanting to share with him this aching happy emotion. Hugh was looking at Celia with all of his heart in his eyes.

Janie's eyes returned to the altar candles. The jets of flame had changed. They were crosses, golden crosses, staggering through a mist of radiance in a blurred uneven line.

☙ III ☙

I

THERE was a Christmas tree, after all, in the living-room of the old brick house. Mrs. Quillen trimmed it for a surprise assisted by Uncle Charlie. It was starred all over with tiny bulbs and the wax angel hung at the top just as it had hung always. The angel and Janie were twins. Uncle Charlie had brought it from Germany for Janie's first Christmas tree.

Christmas day was a happy time; snow and sunshine outside; hope inside, and misty smiles and a letting down after the strain. Mother came home to stay. Hugh whistled in the bath-room again. Rachel cried into the turkey stuffing which didn't hurt it at all. Stoney almost roasted them out so faithfully did he tend the furnace. Celia wore an uplifted expression. Janie smiled her wide gay smile. "Father is better," they told each other at intervals during the day.

There were presents. Janie was awakened by a rough pink tongue ecstatically licking her cheeks. The tongue was part of a small Scotch terrier, ugly and perky and lovable. His eyes were as bright as shoe buttons. One ear stood erect and the other flopped, which gave him a saucy expression. He wore a Scotch plaid collar, banded and buckled with brass. There was a card attached:

> *For a good little egg*
> *From Hugh*

"You darling!" Janie whispered and hugged the small Scotch dog very hard.

"I love him, Hugh," she said at breakfast and smiled her wide gay smile.

"His name is 'Kiltie'." Hugh looked happy this morning. "You can change it if you like."

"It's a lovely name." She was eating breakfast with the small black dog in her lap.

"You mustn't, Janie," Mother said. "You'll teach him very bad manners."

"It's Christmas and Father is better." She made a song of it. The laughing notes, which had for so long been hushed, sprinkled themselves through the air.

Mother smiled and forgot to worry about "Kiltie's" learning bad manners.

"Yes, Father is better," she said.

Rachel, coming in with a pile of golden-brown waffles, looked with glum disapproval at the button eyes and the jaunty ear perked up above the edge of the table.

"Is we all gwine to be pestered wid another dawg?" she inquired of the family at large.

"Do you call that varmint of Celia's a dog?" It was lovely to have Hugh teasing again and smiling his crinkly smile.

"Aunt Rose likes 'Tweedles.'" Celia was admiring the shine of a jeweled bracelet. "I think I'll give him to her."

"Praise Gawd!" Rachel exclaimed and slapped down the plate of waffles.

Later, in the living-room, Hugh thanked Janie for his handkerchiefs.

"Did you really make them?" he asked.

"Every single stitch."

"They're grand. Nobody ever sewed things for me before."

"The initials are wobbly." Janie's expression was apologetic. "Those curly 'K's' are very hard to manage."

"I think they're beautiful." He selected the handkerchief with the most uneven initials and tucked it into the breast pocket of his coat. "I shall wear one every day of my life—right here tucked in with your smile."

He swung her up from the floor and lightly kissed her brow where the chestnut hair grew down in a peak. For a moment the wax angel on the tree seemed to be swimming in a misty blur of green. Then Janie was admiring Celia's gifts and feeling better again.

"I never saw anything so lovely." Celia's fingers were caressing petal-tinted trifles of lace and ribbon and silk.

"It looks like a box of sweet-peas," Janie said admiringly. She read the message on a thick creamy card:

For Hugh's pretty Celia
From Hugh's sister Louise.

Hugh's pretty Celia! It hurt for a moment. Then she could bear it. Perhaps, after a while, it would hurt hardly at all.

"Hugh sent her my picture," Celia was saying. "We were to visit her for New Year's. I suppose it's out of the question now."

"Entirely out of the question." Hugh was standing with his arm around Celia. But out of his breast pocket poked the edge of a handkerchief marked with uneven initials. It was comforting, for some peculiar reason that Janie could not understand.

"I wanted to go," Celia sighed.

"It's nicer here," Hugh said contentedly. "Mulberry Square, after all, is sort of an interesting place."

A fretful shadow slipped across Celia's face. It was gone in a moment. Janie saw it. Hugh could not have seen it at all. He was looking at Celia's hair, honey-colored and silky, caught in a knot at the nape of her neck.

Christmas day was a happy time. The days which followed were pleasant, too. Janie was permitted to stay, each afternoon, a little longer with Father. She took Kiltie to see him. Together they laughed at the ear which perked and the ear which flopped down. One day Father was strong enough to throw a ball across the room and to pull it from the tenacious grasp of Kiltie's sharp white teeth. His arms were strong, Janie noticed. But he never moved his legs.

"Do they hurt you, Father?" she asked.

"Not much."

"You never move them."

"They deserve a vacation," he said lightly. "They've been very faithful for more than fifty years."

He threw the ball for Kiltie, then, and in a moment Janie was laughing with him at the frisking small black dog. Father was certainly better. They talked about the fishing trip to Canada next June.

"You'll have to walk, Janie. Not even horses can get through those forest trails."

"I can walk." She thought of walking with Father beside her, Father brown and healthy in his flannel shirt and corduroy trousers. She was sure that she wouldn't mind the walking at all.

"Polish up on your French."

"Why?"

"The Indian guides speak French."

"Je vous aime." Her accent was very bad.

"Look here!" Father pretended to be alarmed. "Are you going to make love to Indian guides?"

"That was for you." She laid her cheek against his.

"Je vous aime." Father returned the compliment. His accent was even worse.

But they weren't concerned with accents. Father was getting better. Every afternoon when she left he said:

"Tell Rachel to stir up some waffle batter. I'm coming home pretty soon."

Then, at the end of the week, they learned that Father would not come home. Doctor Alden told them. He sat beside the living-room fire and told them as kindly as he could that Father might never walk again.

It was something about the spine. Janie, curled up in a corner of the davenport, told herself that he couldn't be talking about Father. But he was. He was telling them that Father might have to live in a rolling chair. There was a chance, he said. If Father might be removed to a private hospital in New York. He mentioned the name of a specialist. He talked of an operation.

Mother rocked back and forth. Celia sobbed hysterically. Doctor Alden mopped his brow as though the room were very hot. Janie looked up at Hugh. He was standing beside the window. His face against the dull blue drape was white and drawn.

"Could Doctor Ballard be removed?" Hugh asked evenly. His hands were knotted into fists. The vein in his forehead was throbbing.

Doctor Alden thought that would be possible. In a week or two Father would be strong enough to endure the trip. He would make the necessary arrangements. Mrs. Ballard would want to go?

Mother was uncertain.

"Oh, Mother," Janie cried. "He would be so lonely alone."

"Of course, Mother," Celia said. "We can manage here at home."

"Good girls!" Doctor Alden smiled at Celia. He smiled at Janie. He blew his nose.

They discussed it after he had gone.

"The money ——" Mother said. "There's never more than just enough. You know how Father is."

"I can arrange that, Mrs. Ballard." Hugh's eyes were somber. All his gayety was gone.

"But Hugh ——" Mother protested faintly. "We can't let you ——"

"This isn't a question of money," said Hugh. "It's a question of happiness."

"You—you're sweet, Hugh." Celia's eyes were like rain-drenched violets. The silver harp strings were quivering.

Janie looked at Hugh with a world of tenderness in her eyes. But Hugh was looking at Celia with the firelight shining across her hair.

There was a family conference that evening.

Aunt Lucy was present and Uncle Frank, Aunt
Rhoda, Uncle Bradford and Great-aunt Rose.
Great-uncle Charlie was not invited. But Great-
uncle Charlie came, too. They were all very much
distressed. The ladies wept and the gentlemen
cleared their throats.

"Hugh has offered to arrange for the expenses,"
Mother said anxiously. "But it seems to me it's a
family matter and ——"

"Hugh will soon be a member of the family."
The jet butterflies had vanished with the summer.
The purple glass grapes on Aunt Rose's toque tin-
kled only a faint approval. Hugh would come into
money, of course. But the Charleston Shelbys!
Well, it was greatly to be regretted.

"It hardly seems the thing to do," Mother worried. "I don't think John ——"

Uncle Bradford looked uneasy and talked about
the stock market. Aunt Rose regretted that, after
all, her income was inadequate. Aunt Lucy looked
at Uncle Frank.

"Let me take care of it, Helen," he said. Already he was reaching for check-book and pen.

"That's very kind of you, Frank."

"It's nothing, nothing." He patted Mother's
shoulder. "Glad to help. Always glad to help."
Uncle Frank's ruddy features were wreathed in satisfaction. For, twenty-five years ago, his money
had been a source of discomfort, now it was proving
its worth.

"Well, here's to mules and the Civil War!" Uncle Charlie, seated with Janie on the Chesterfield in the hall, raised an invisible glass.

"You mustn't, Uncle Charlie."

"Simple gratitude, my dear." The old man's waggish smile was softened and subdued. "I might have been obliged to sell my last three bottles of sherry wine."

So the arrangements were made. Father was to be taken to New York as soon as he was strong enough to endure the trip.

"The chances are favorable," said the jolly round doctor.

"He has a splendid heart," said the solemn one with the beard.

Father had been told. Janie knew as soon as she saw him when she went to the hospital with Hugh on New Year's eve. His face was whiter than it had been. There was a look of patience in his eyes which was very hard to bear. But he smiled at them and ran his fingers through Kiltie's coat.

"I'm going away," he said.

"Yes, Father." Tears spilled down over Janie's cheeks. Hugh turned and stared out the window.

Father smiled with that look of unbearable patience.

"Legs aren't important," he said.

"Father!" A heart-broken little cry.

"There's a good chance, Doctor Ballard."
Hugh's knuckles showed white through the tan.

"Legs aren't important," Father repeated. "I
can use Janie's and Stoney's and ——"

"And mine," Hugh offered brokenly. "I wish I
could give them to you."

"They'd run the rest of me ragged." It was
like Father to make it easy for them. Legs aren't
important! Never to walk again . . .

"It isn't so bad." Father smiled at them both.
"If we can wake them up, all well and good." He
touched his useless legs. "If we can't—well, I
won't have to run for trains or buy new shoes
or ——"

"I'll stay here as long as you need me." Hugh's
hand was clasped in Father's.

"Thank you, my boy. I never questioned that."

"I'll stay," Hugh repeated huskily. "I'll do the
best I can."

II

"Do you think we should, Aunt Lucy?" Janie
was talking at the telephone in the hall.

"What is it?" Celia asked, pausing on the stairs.

Janie covered the mouthpiece with her hand.

"Muriel has some guests from Washington.
Aunt Lucy wants us to come out for the evening.
It isn't really a party. Tom will be there and

Dolly Bruce and the Washington people and Carter
Shelby ———"

Janie saw Celia's expression change. Her hand
on the banister trembled and was still.

"I don't see why we shouldn't," she said
casually.

"But Hugh has office hours even on New Year's
day."

"He can come out later." Celia's cheeks were
flushed. There was an eagerness in her eyes. "Will
Aunt Lucy send William for us?"

Janie nodded.

"Then tell her, Yes." Celia was flying upstairs.
"Father wouldn't want us to stay at home here and
brood."

Janie was ready first. She went into Celia's room.
There were signs of haste and indecision. The contents of the wardrobe were strewn across the bed
and the chairs. Celia, in a slim black frock, was
smoothing her hair at the dressing-table.

"Don't wear that," Janie said sharply. The slim
black frock looked theatrical. Celia was posing
again.

"I couldn't bear the gay ones." Celia's eyes in
the mirror were bright with tears.

Janie felt ashamed of herself. She had thought
that Celia must know how fragile she looked in
the plain black dress with her creamy skin and the
pale soft gold of her hair. But Celia was thinking

of Father. And Celia had been sweet. Janie made
an important announcement.

"I'm not going back to college."

"Why not?" Celia asked absently.

"You'd be lonely here after Mother has gone."
It was pleasant to be able to love Celia again. She
had been so dear and unaffected ever since Father
was hurt. "I couldn't bear it," she added, "to be
so far away." She edged closer to Celia and slipped
an arm around her shoulders. "I'd rather stay
here with you."

"Funny little brown girl!" Celia did not look
at Janie. She was using a lipstick lightly. Her
hand trembled a little.

There were lights in "Sportsman's Hall." Aunt
Lucy met them at the door.

"You shouldn't stay home all the time," she said
with an arm around each. "You're pale, Celia."

"I don't sleep well," Celia murmured. Carter
Shelby, tall and graceful and dark, had left the
group around the fireplace, was walking to meet
them across the hall.

"It's nice to see you again." He was smiling
down at Celia, holding both of her hands.

"Thank you, Carter." Celia lifted a wan lovely
face. "We've had an unhappy time."

"And this is—Janie."

"Good-evening, Mr. Shelby." Janie greeted him
stiffly. She hated it because Celia had given him
both of her hands. Hugh was at home in the office

and Celia was letting this Carter Shelby hold both
of her pretty hands. But she mustn't spy on Celia.
It wasn't exactly fair.

A maid took their wraps. They joined the group
around the fire. There were introductions. Tom
pushed forward a chair for Celia. Janie sat on a
cushion and hugged her knees in her arms. Carter
Shelby devoted himself to Muriel. He sat with her
on an oak settee beside the hearth, lit her cigarettes,
talked to her in an undertone which excluded the
rest of the party. Muriel seemed to be satisfied
with the arrangement. The rose of her velvet
frock made a faint color in her cheeks. Her eyes,
when she glanced at Carter, were warm and faintly
amused.

Tom and the two sleek young men from Washington, whose names were Ted and Jerry, devoted
themselves to Celia. Dolly Bruce, small and dark
and vivacious, chattered to the girl from Washington, a pallid ash-blonde named Laura in a gown of
silver tissue.

"We're used to it," Janie heard Dolly say.
"Celia is the belle of our rural hamlet."

"She's pretty—if you care for the type." The
pallid Laura gestured with a cigarette holder enameled in emerald green. Her eyes furtively watched
the sleek young man named Ted who was devoting
himself to Celia.

"She's engaged," Dolly confided. "She's going
to marry her father's assistant."

"Oh, really!" Janie thought that the pallid Laura looked decidedly relieved. "She is pretty." Her voice was more enthusiastic. "The madonna look always gets them. Men are such utter fools."

Celia was more than pretty, Janie thought, with the dull tapestry of the chair making a background for her head. She sat with her hands linked loosely in her lap and talked very little. Occasionally she smiled at one of the attentive young men. Her eyes strayed at intervals to the shadowy corner where Muriel sat with Carter Shelby. Janie wondered what she was thinking. It was impossible even to guess.

Dolly presently turned the radio knobs. Music crashed into the quiet of the oak-beamed hall. The young man named Ted danced with Laura. The young man named Jerry whirled Dolly away. Carter Shelby left the settee and drew Celia up from her chair. Janie slipped into the vacant place beside Muriel. Tom joined them.

"You can fight for me, children," he said.

"Too lazy." Muriel flicked the ash from her cigarette.

Tom laughed. He bent his curly dark head.

"Gamble for it," he said. "Whoever pulls out the longer hair wins."

"Couldn't think of it." Muriel smiled. "Your hair is your greatest beauty."

The sacrilege was prevented. Uncle Frank called from the library door.

"Can I speak to you, Tom?"

"Certainly, Mr. Grove." Tom turned away from the fire, strode briskly across the hall.

"Remember when Tom used to mow the grass?" Janie asked, settling herself comfortably on the long upholstered settee.

"He was the Sir Galahad of my youthful dreams," Muriel said with a sigh.

"Isn't he still?"

"I think he's splendid." Muriel gazed at her fingertips. "I shall always be fond of Tom."

"Does he know you like him?" Janie presently asked. Some men were stupid about such things. There, for instance, was Hugh.

"He should," Muriel said frankly. "I've told him dozens of times."

"What does he say?"

"He calls me a forward brat or something equally tender." Muriel smiled at Janie. "I get discouraged at times."

They watched the dancers moving about through the dimly lighted hall. Celia and Carter were handsome together. The others suffered by contrast. Celia's small blonde head glinted against Carter's well-tailored dinner coat. He bent a little toward her. They danced slowly, rhythmically, out of shadowy corners, through pools of shaded light, into the shadows again.

"Does Celia love Hugh?" Muriel suddenly asked.

"She's engaged to him, isn't she?" Janie's heart beat swiftly. She felt that her cheeks were flushed.

"Don't be quaint, little girl."

"Gracious, then, how do I know?"

"They will be married in June?"

"When Hugh's year with Father is finished." Hugh and Celia. Celia and Hugh. Getting married and going away together. Janie would be a bridesmaid. Hugh and Celia. Celia and Hugh . . .

"What did you say, Muriel?"

"Tom's funny about her engagement," Muriel repeated. "I thought he would be hurt. Maybe he is. He doesn't seem to mind . . . Carter dances beautifully," she added as Celia and Carter moved again into the light.

"Do you like him?" Janie asked.

"It's been fun to know him in Washington," Muriel answered lightly. "He's rather ornamental." She was silent for a moment and then she said with sudden intensity. "Yes, Janie, I like him very much."

Janie wondered if Muriel cared because Carter was dancing with Celia. She glanced up at her swiftly. Muriel was leaning against the high dark back of the oak settee, her legs indolently crossed, the rose of her velvet frock casting a faint color over her cheeks. Her eyes were tranquil and ever so faintly amused. What was she thinking?

Muriel was thinking of the words Carter had whispered when he left her to dance with Celia.

"I owe a great deal to Celia," he had said with his charming low voice setting the words to music. "But for her, I might not have known you."

Carter had stressed the pronoun. He was made that way. It was something he could not help.

III

"It's nice to dance with you again." Carter stressed the pronoun.

"I like it, too." The silver harp strings quivered.

" 'Come with me where moon-beams . . .' " Carter sang very softly the words of the lilting waltz. "Remember—Celia? They played it last summer at the shore."

"That was a long time ago." Her left hand fluttered away from his shoulder, rested against her throat. Glancing down, his eyes caught the shine of the ring on her slim third finger.

"Is that a warning?" he asked.

"I'm engaged, you know." It pleased her to say it. It pleased her because she was fragile and lovely in the slim little black crêpe frock.

"I got drunk the night that I heard." It pleased him to exaggerate a bit because, after all, there was the ring on her finger and she was very lovely in the slim little plain black frock.

"Oh, Carter!" The violet eyes reproached him. "You shouldn't do things like that."

"I had to—forget." He held her close because—well, there was the ring on her finger and her head against his shoulder was small and fragrant and blonde. "Will he make you happy?" he asked as they danced into the shadows again.

"Who?" She pretended to misunderstand.

"This red-haired young doctor."

"He's sweet." The pleased dreamy expression crept into her lifted eyes. "We shall go abroad for a year."

"I should have liked to show you beautiful places." His voice was touchingly sad. "Paris. The Mediterranean. The Italian lakes."

His manner indicated that Celia had been to blame. She preferred to believe that was true. His eyes were ardent and tender. Her beauty stirred him. It gave her a thrilling sense of power. She found herself feeling sorry for this charming young man who hadn't quite measured up to her high ideals.

"If things had been different," she murmured vaguely and dropped her head against his shoulder.

"If things had been different," he repeated and held her very close. "Are you happy, Celia?"

"I've been unhappy about Father." The silver harp strings were trembling again.

"I'm sorry. You were made for happiness, my dear."

"I want to be happy." She looked up at him with eyes brimming over with tears. "I feel unhappiness so."

"If there is ever anything I can do ——" His voice trailed off into silence, promising many things.

"Thank you, Carter," Celia murmured. "I shall think of you as my—friend."

They had moved into a shadowy corner. The fire and the lights were very far away. He stooped swiftly and kissed the creamy hollow of her throat.

"That's for remembrance, my lovely lost Celia," he said.

He was made that way. It was something he could not help.

IV

Hugh was sitting in the armchair beside the living-room fire when Janie and Celia returned from "Sportsman's Hall." His tired eyes brightened. He rose and crossed to the door.

"I've just gotten back," he said. "I 'phoned. They said you had left."

"William brought us home." Celia's manner was detached. She turned toward the stairs.

"You aren't going up just yet?" Hugh asked wistfully.

"I'm sleepy." Celia patted back a dainty yawn.

"But I haven't seen you all day." Hugh made a motion with his arms. Celia edged ever so slightly towards the stairs. Janie fumbled with the buckles on her galoshes. They seemed unusually hard to manage. Perhaps that was because she couldn't see them very well.

"It isn't my fault." Celia implied that she had been neglected and Hugh was entirely to blame. "I'm very tired. I want to go up to bed."

"Good-night, then, Beautiful." He stooped to kiss her. His lips merely brushed her cheek.

"Good-night, Hugh."

"What?" There was a note of fear in his voice.

"Good-night—darling."

"That's better. Happy dreams, my sweet."

Celia moved away from the door. Her hand rested against her throat as though it held there something precious which might be lost. Her heels made a tapping sound on the polished steps. Upstairs a door closed gently.

"Want something to eat?" Janie asked, a hurt in her heart because the brightness was gone and Hugh's brown eyes were somber and weary again.

"Aren't you sleepy, too?" he inquired.

Her head shook a gallant negation. She struggled against a yawn.

"Poke up the fire," she said gently. "I'll find us something to eat."

IV

I

FATHER was removed to New York at the end of January. Mother accompanied him, leaving behind her all sort of instructions and worries and prophecies. The matter of Janie's return to college had been the subject of many discussions. Janie had been firm. She didn't want to go back this year.

"It will save expense," Mother said with a resigned expression as they sat together in the living-room her last night at home. "We can't let Hugh or Uncle Frank do any more for us. But Father wanted you to go on, Janie."

"Father understands." Janie was sitting close to Mother on a hassock beside her chair. "And I will go on," she promised. "I'll send for my books and study every day. Doctor Warden will help me with Latin and I can read French with Professor Mantell."

"I wish you wouldn't go there," Mother fretted. "Those Mantells are shiftless and not even decently clean."

191

"He'll help me with French." Janie tried not to
be indignant because it was Mother's last night at
home. "I can take the exams next fall and go on
with my class. I couldn't bear it to be so far away
from home."

Mother sighed and looked as though it was all
too dreadful to be endured and warned Celia about
taking cold and made Janie promise not to go near
Vine or Juniper street while the flu epidemic was
raging and clung to them at bedtime with tears in
her pretty blue eyes.

"You'll write to us every day," Janie implored
with her arms around Mother's neck.

"Every day," Mother promised.

"And telegraph," Celia added, "as soon as
the ——"

They couldn't speak of the operation. They
clung together in the upstairs hall, Mother and
Celia and Janie, faced with an uncertain future,
wondering if ever they would all be happy again.

"You'll have to be careful about money," Mother
said with a worried frown. "Tom McAllister is
going over Father's accounts. He'll explain things
to you."

"We will be careful," Janie assured her. "I'll go
to market myself and make Rachel use left-overs
and turn off lights and be a regular tyrant around
this house."

"I did want a nice wedding for Celia," Mother
said wistfully.

As though it would matter, Janie thought, what
kind of a wedding you had if you were getting married to Hugh.

"Don't worry about that." Celia relinquished
orange blossoms and a satin train and a tunnel of
awning in front of the church. "We must think
only of Father." She looked noble and self-sac-
rificing with tears on her lashes and shadows under
her eyes.

"You're so brave, darling," Mother marveled.
And somehow it seemed more wonderful that Celia
should relinquish the satin train than that Janie
should study alone and go to market and turn off
lights. Janie's gallantry was silent. Celia's came
with a blowing of trumpets and a beating of many
drums.

Mrs. Quillen was reinstalled in the old brick
house. Life settled into a quiet routine. "Sportsman's Hall" had been closed again. The Groves
had returned to Washington. Hugh was kept very
busy. The flu epidemic had crept through Vine
and Juniper streets up into the Square. Hugh
snatched hasty meals at irregular hours and slept
scarcely at all.

"You're working too hard," Celia said one day
with a pretty air of concern.

"I must." The angle of Hugh's jaw was lean
and square and determined.

"Can't you go out to Dolly's with me to-night?"

Celia sat on the arm of his chair, twisting around her finger a lock of his rumpled bright hair.

"Is it a party?" Hugh asked wearily.

"Just two tables of bridge," Celia explained. "I haven't been anywhere for ages," she added with a sigh.

"I can't, darling. I'd flop on the table and snore."

"There's no use killing yourself." Celia's expression was fretful.

"It was my fault." The vein in Hugh's forehead was throbbing.

"That's morbid, Hugh."

"It's honest, at any rate." He was looking at her strangely. Celia's expression changed.

"I know, darling," she said softly. "You're sweet, Hugh."

"Do you love me, Celia?" He pulled her down into his arms.

"Of course." She looked up at him and smiled. She wore her "Saint Cecilia" expression. Beneath it she thrilled at the worship in his eyes. It gave her again that thrilling sense of power. If you were beautiful you could take what you wanted from life . . .

"Just me, I mean," Hugh continued earnestly. "Not the money my father left or ——"

"Hugh!" Her eyes reproached him. There was in her expression a hint of the hidden loveliness which held him with its promise. Some day he would find it, the real loveliness of Celia, hidden beneath her moods and pretty poses.

"I love you so much," he said.

"I love you, Hugh."

She was quiet in his arms, her eyes dreaming off into the distance.

"What are you thinking?" he asked, hoping to catch a glimpse of the real lovely Celia.

"Will you take me to Paris, Hugh?" Her voice was warm with anticipation. "And Venice? Dolly Bruce is so superior because she has been to Venice."

Hugh's expectations were dashed. He blamed himself. He hadn't yet been able to reach her. It would be easier when he had more time, when he wasn't always so sleepy. He did not blame Celia for the accident. He blamed his jealousy, his fear that he might lose her. His love for her was a madness. He hadn't thought it would be like that. He wanted love to be sane and beautiful, a warm steady emotion, like a fire on a friendly hearth . . .

"What are *you* thinking?" Celia asked, her lips against his cheek.

He wasn't thinking. He was breathing the fragrance of her hair, feeling the petal smoothness of her skin. There was a hammering in his ears.

"I love you, love you," he said.

A glint of satisfaction sparkled in Celia's eyes. Hugh did not see it.

The days lengthened into weeks. Janie busied herself with going to market and keeping accounts and writing a long letter to Father every day. She toiled patiently over her books and read French in the evening with Professor Mantell who was often tipsy and always entertaining. She watched over Hugh with a motherly air of concern. She conferred with Rachel and Mrs. Quillen over household matters which had to do with coal bills and plumbing and beef loaf instead of chicken. She had an interview with Tom McAllister.

"It's pretty much of a muddle." Tom sat in Father's office chair before a desk strewn with papers.

"You mean there are bills?" Janie asked.

"Your father is a saint on earth," Tom said impatiently, "but he hasn't, so far as I have been able to discover, an ounce of business sense." He opened the shabby ledger. "Some of these accounts have been standing for fifteen years."

"Can you do anything about it?"

"There are notes in the bank." Tom's brows drew together in a frown. "He has made himself responsible for every Tom, Dick and Harry in town."

Janie knew very little about notes. She thought they were something which had to be paid. She suggested to Tom that he pay them at once.

"What do we use for money?" Tom fluttered the pages of the ledger.

Janie paled.

"Isn't there any?" she asked. There had always

been money enough. They had lived very well in
the old brick house in the Square. Father never
mentioned money. He hated to bother about it.

"Don't look so tragic." Tom smiled away his
frown. "I'll collect what I can. Perhaps we can
set it all straight before your father comes home.
Just try to be careful and don't run up any staggering bills."

Janie flung herself into a frenzy of economizing.
They decided to dismiss the office girl.

"Celia and I can take turns," Janie suggested.
"It will give us something to do."

Celia agreed. She bought herself white uniforms
and wished she might wear a Red Cross arrangement on her head. The uniforms were becoming.
At first she was interested and amused. Then the
monotony became irksome. She fainted one evening, during office hours.

"I'm sorry," she murmured when she opened her
eyes to find herself on the living-room davenport
surrounded by anxious faces. "It was the smell,
I think."

"Never mind, Celia." Hugh was holding her
wrist. "Your pulse is normal." He looked at her
searchingly.

"I—I feel so faint." Her voice was a whisper.

"She's as pale as a ghost!" Mrs. Quillen made
fanning motions with a folded wad of newspaper.
"There ain't no color at all in her face."

Janie touched Celia's cheek with the tip of her
finger. Powder! Her suspicions were confirmed.
She glanced up at Hugh and saw, with feeling of
alarm, that he had suspected, too. She hid the
tell-tale finger in the pocket of her dress.

"I wanted to help," Celia murmured. Her eyes,
wide and appealing, were fixed on Hugh's stern face.
Janie saw the stern expression soften. Hugh
stooped and kissed Celia's brow. Janie, watching
intently, saw Celia's lips curve into a smile.

Hugh went abruptly out of the room. Had he
seen that smile? All evening he was unusually
quiet. After office hours were over, Janie walked
with him into the hall. Celia was talking at the
telephone. She placed the receiver on the hook
when she saw Hugh watching her and adopted a
languid air.

"Dolly wants me to stay with her to-night," she
said. "They're driving in for me. I think it would
do me good to get away."

"Perhaps," Hugh said brusquely. The set of his
lips filled Janie with sudden fright.

"Will you come with us?" Celia asked, rising
from the Chesterfield to slip her arm through his
and smile coaxingly up into his eyes.

"I can't," he said briefly. "I have some reading
to do."

But he didn't read. He paced the floor of his
room upstairs. Janie, playing double solitaire with

Mrs. Quillen in the living-room below, heard his footsteps treading endlessly back and forth.

"What ails him to-night?" Mrs. Quillen asked with an eloquent glance toward the ceiling.

"I don't know," Janie answered. That wasn't quite true. She thought that Hugh had suspected Celia. She thought that the fainting fit had not deceived him at all. What would happen? What would he do? . . .

"Janie, Janie, you can't be puttin' a red queen there."

"Of course you can't. I'm sorry, Mrs. Quillen."

Janie served as office girl, after the evening that Celia fainted. She didn't really mind. It was pleasant to be with Hugh. Celia's uniforms were a trifle long. She hemmed them up and took tucks in the sleeves.

The arrival of the postman was an event of great importance. There were letters from Mother every day and sometimes a note from Father. He wrote to them cheerfully, illustrated the messages with small ridiculous drawings. He was getting stronger. The operation was to be performed in a very short time. There was nothing to do except wait.

Occasionally a square gray envelope came in with the rest of the mail. Carter Shelby was writing to Celia again. Celia tucked the letters away with a casual air and seldom mentioned his name. But she watched for the square gray envelopes. Janie was sure of that. And all through February while the snow changed to sleet and mud and each gray day that passed seemed drearier than the others, Janie watched for a telegram from Mother.

The telegram never arrived. One morning, early in March, a letter came addressed in Mother's writing to Hugh. He read it at breakfast, sitting in Father's chair, with the wintry sunshine streaming in across the table.

"It's over," he said.

"The operation?" Celia's hands crept up to her heart.

Janie's eyes asked a question. Hugh looked at her miserably. He looked away. But he had to tell them.

"It was unsuccessful," he said.

"You mean ——" Celia faltered.

"He will never walk again."

Janie made a faint little moan and her fingers twisted together.

"He'll be well otherwise?" Celia asked.

"Yes." Hugh's voice was husky and rough. "He may live for years."

"Is he coming home?" Janie asked.

"Not at once. They want to keep him there for observation."

"It isn't so bad," Celia said slowly as though she were reassuring herself. "He will have Stoney to take care of him."

"Not so bad!" Hugh turned to her almost

Hugh looked at Celia.   He looked away.

"I want to," he said simply.

II

Janie lay on the hearth in front of the living-room fire, propped up sidewise on her elbow, her cheek in the palm of her hand.   The other hand stroked Kiltie, curled up on a cushion beside her. Celia wandered restlessly around the room, touched the piano keys, fluttered the pages of a magazine on the table, pulled back the window hangings.

"It's sleeting," she said.   The silver harp strings jangled.

"Hugh ought to be back pretty soon," Janie said drowsily.

"Hugh is simply morbid.   I believe he enjoys being a martyr."

"Celia!"   There was a note of reproach in Janie's husky young voice.

"He has no right to sacrifice himself, to sacrifice ——" She paused abruptly.

Janie knew she was thinking of herself.   Celia hated the Square.

"I think he's splendid," she said warmly.

"Of course he is," Celia dropped into the arm-chair beside the fire.   "I feel so miserable," she said. "I've cried myself sick about Father."

Celia stared at the flames.   Janie stroked Kiltie's rough coat.   The quiet of the room was broken only by the sleet against the windows, the snapping of the logs, the dull ticking of the onyx clock on the mantel.

"I've been thinking," Janie presently said, "that we could fix over the parlour into a room for Father."

"The parlour," Celia repeated absently.

"It would be hard for him to get up and down stairs." Janie swallowed and continued. "We could make it into a cheerful room and have a door cut through into the office and Stoney could sleep in there on a cot." Janie's face brightened with enthusiasm. "We could have it re-papered and hang new curtains and bring down Father's mahogany bed and ——"

"A bed in the parlour?" Celia shivered.

"I think it would be nice." Janie enlarged upon the plan which had been taking shape all day in her busy head. "I have the Christmas money Aunt Lucy gave me and so have you. We could do it for a surprise. Father could see people in the office and wheel himself out into the dining-room for meals and ——"

"Janie! How can you?" Celia interrupted.

"How can I what?"

"Talk about it so casually." Celia's face was as white as a blanched almond; her hands were clasped tightly over her heart. "How can you think of turning the parlour into a sick room? People don't have beds in the parlour except on Juniper street."

"But Father won't be exactly sick." Janie tried to explain. "And he'll still be Father. We could make it look like a sitting-room except for the bed and ——"

"Hush!" Celia said sharply.

Janie glanced up, her eyes wide with surprise. Celia reconsidered. The white fury in her face softened perceptibly.

"I can't bear it!" she said brokenly. "You don't mind such things, Janie dear. Sickness, ugliness tortures me. I simply can't bear it, that's all."

Janie didn't mind! The thought of Father in a chair was like a knife through her heart. The thought that now they could never tramp through the Canadian forest to Father's beautiful lake filled her with misery. Janie didn't mind! It was because she minded so terribly that she wanted to fix over a room for Father. But she couldn't tell Celia. She couldn't explain.

The clock ticked away the moments. The logs crackled. The sleet rattled against the windows. What was Celia thinking as she sat so white and silent in the arm-chair beside the hearth? Why couldn't she always be natural and sweet as she had been just after Father was hurt? It was the excitement of that time, Janie thought. Celia could rise to an emergency. She couldn't endure the dragging monotonous days. But if she really loved Hugh? She didn't love Hugh. Janie realized it with a sharp feeling of alarm. When you loved people

you wanted to make them happy. And it was
Celia's fault really. Not Hugh's. He would be
terribly hurt. He was so honest and sincere. Hugh
would be hurt and Janie, who loved him so much,
could do nothing to help. She flopped over on the
hearth and buried her face in Kiltie's rough coat.
Oh, Hugh! Oh, dear big Hugh who never laughed
any more . . .

He came in at midnight. He looked completely
exhausted. But his eyes brightened as he saw them
waiting for him beside the fire.

"I didn't expect this," he said. "I thought you
would both be in bed." He smiled wearily. The
smile caught at Janie's heart. It reminded her of
Father's smile. She realized, all at once, that Hugh
was like Father in many ways. She hadn't thought
of it before.

"You didn't mean it, Hugh?" Celia had left the
armchair. Her hands were clinging to the lapels
of his coat. "You didn't mean that you would stay
on here in the Square?"

"Of course I meant it." There again was that
finality in his voice. "I'm tired, Celia. Must we
talk about it to-night?"

"Yes," Celia said firmly. "You can't sacrifice
your whole life. It's morbid. It's unnecessary.
You can't do it, Hugh."

"Does it matter so very much?" He led her to
the davenport, drew her with a weary sigh down

into the circle of his arm. "Let's just be quiet to-night."

"Listen to me, Hugh."

"Please, darling . . ."

Hugh's weary sigh, his look of patience was more than Janie could bear.

"Celia!" It was an almost soundless protest. But Celia heard. She looked at Janie. There was no mistaking her meaning. Janie slipped out of the room with Kiltie hugged tight in her arms.

III

"Why, Janie Ballard!"

Janie, huddled into a heap on the stairs, blinked and opened her eyes.

"I thought you had gone to bed." Celia sounded cross.

"I was sleepy," Janie murmured. "I couldn't get any farther."

"It's one o'clock."

One o'clock! Then Celia must have been talking to Hugh for an hour.

"You come straight on up to bed." Celia brushed past her huddled figure.

"I'll have to take Kiltie out in the kitchen."

Celia's heels made a clicking sound on the steps. A door opened and closed. Janie, with Kiltie in her arms, sat quite still on the stairs. The light from the living-room fire shone out across the hall.

She heard a sound of somebody moving, the creak of the davenport springs, a long weary sigh. Hugh!

She walked quietly to the door. Hugh had flung himself down on the davenport. The position of his body suggested complete exhaustion. His eyes were wide awake, tortured ruddy brown eyes which stared at the dying fire.

"Hugh," she called softly.

His eyes turned from the fire, brightened, were somber again.

"I thought you had gone to bed."

"Aren't you sleepy, Hugh?"

"All but my head. That keeps on spinning around."

"Do you want something hot to drink?"

He shook his head. He looked at Janie, sleepy and small in the doorway, tender concern in her wide clear hazel eyes. A brown little girl with a dog. Sweet, funny kid!

"Come here," he said.

She crossed at once to the davenport with the small black dog hugged tight in her arms. She looked at him with a tenderness in her eyes. She said nothing at all.

"Stay with me," Hugh said wistfully. "I hate being alone."

She made a nest of cushions on the floor and settled herself among them. Her arm, resting against the edge of the davenport, formed a pillow for her head. By lifting her eyes a little she could look directly at Hugh.   Kiltie whimpered, nuzzled, fell asleep in her lap.

"Am I being heroic?" Hugh asked.   "Tell me, Janie.   You always seem to know about things. You don't really know," he added.   "You feel. How do you feel about that?"

"Heroic?"

"Is it morbid of me to *want* to stay here and help your father?"   She knew that he was repeating things which Celia had said.   "Have I a martyr complex?   Is it a theatrical gesture?   Tell me, young fellow."

"I think it's splendid," she said.

He liked that.   He had liked her to admire him doing stunts on the hickory limbs.   He was only a boy who had made a mistake and wanted to make up for it.   Janie felt very mature.

"I really want to, Janie," Hugh said earnestly. "I couldn't leave him.   No matter what it costs ———"

Costs!   Janie was breathless and still.

"It's the disappointment."   Hugh seemed to have forgotten Janie.   He was talking to relieve his own overburdened mind.   "It is hard for her. She loves gayety.   She wants to go abroad."

Janie made no comment.   She just nestled closer until her head lay in the curve of his arm.   He was stroking her hair.   She could feel his fingers.   Like Father's fingers, gentle and firm and caressing with a touch that made her tingle as Father's fingers had never done. A wave of happiness swept through her, a wave of misery. Hugh was caressing her hair!

"I didn't think she would take it like this," Hugh said presently. "I thought she would understand. But it doesn't matter. Even if I lose her, this is something that I am going to do."

Janie saw his lips close in a determined line. She saw the torture in his eyes. She had to help him somehow.

"I guess," she said slowly, "if you are as beautiful as Celia you do expect more from life. You can't bear commonplace things—like Mulberry Square. Especially," she added, "if you've been taught to expect it all of your life."

She was thinking of the people who had taught Celia to believe that she was sacred and set apart; Mother, Aunt Rose, the boys who had loved her. She had often thought that it wasn't entirely Celia's fault. She had never expressed it in words before. For years she had kept that thought tucked away in the back of her mind so that it might comfort Hugh to-night.

It did comfort him. A look of peace crept into his eyes.

"It's there," he said drowsily. "The hidden beauty. I'll find it some time."

He was quiet for so long that Janie thought he

had gone to sleep. She glanced up at him. The look of peace had vanished from his eyes. They stared somberly over Janie's head into the glowing flames. Presently he said only half aloud, "But suppose it isn't there. Suppose I made it up . . . mirage . . ."

Janie gasped and sat very still.

"No, that's not true," Hugh said firmly. "I'm not being fair. But Janie darling, I can't play games."

"Games?" she asked, bewildered.

"It's a waste," he continued slowly. "I want to live serenely, honestly. I—I can't bear scenes."

There would be many scenes. Janie was sure of that. Celia had a gift for creating scenes. Hugh would be hurt over and over again. It made her wretched to think that Hugh would be hurt. She loved him and she was helpless. There was nothing she could do. She rested her cheek against his hand and winked back the stinging tears.

"What would I do without you?" Hugh asked. "How could I bear it at all?"

"Silly!" she whispered, a happy feeling in her heart because there was, after all, something she could do for Hugh. He needed her a little. He needed her very much.

"Don't leave me," he said, "if I happen to go to sleep."

"I won't," she promised.

"You're a joy in the world, little fellow." The words came very slowly. "There isn't much to you except your hazel eyes and your lovely smile," he added, smiling at the drowsy droop of her lashes. "But I like you in spite of that. You're a very good little egg."

V

I

CELIA wandered restlessly from window to window in her cream and lilac room. Spring called to her in the rustle of the wind through the new leaves on the locusts, in the tune of the hurdy-gurdy, in the shrill voices of little girls skipping rope along the sidewalk . . . "Salt, vinegar, mustard, pepper!" . . . She watched them absently; little girls with thick underwear showing when their skirts flapped up, little boys in ragged sweaters swarming through the Square. Her delicate nostrils flared in an expression of disdain. It was all so shabby and down at the heel. She couldn't bear it another day, this dingy common old Square.

Hugh was simply impossible. In all the weeks since he had announced his intention of staying on the Square, she had not been able to shake his determination. There were times when he had wavered, times when she had been almost confident of success. But he had never entirely yielded.

"You're sacrificing your future, Hugh."

"I can't see it that way."

"Father wouldn't expect it."

"I shall stay as long as he needs me."

"Don't you love me?"

"I adore you. But this is something that I intend to do."

How she hated the finality in his voice, the tight line of his lips, the stubborn thrust of his jaw. It was absurd, unreasonable. She was sorry about Father, too. But Hugh's sense of duty or honor or whatever he called it was fantastic. Nothing had been able to shake his determination. She had stopped wearing his ring. He had noticed it but had said nothing at all. He seemed purposely to neglect and avoid her. He shut himself into his room or drove with Janie in that outrageous car they called "Horatius." It was more than anybody could be expected to stand.

Nothing had been able to shake his determination. His sister Louise, a tall beautiful woman with red hair darker than Hugh's, had come to reason with him. She had been cordial to Celia. Together they had attempted to make Hugh see that he was bent on ruining his life. Louise had stormed and cajoled and offered him bribes. She had suggested that they take her husband's yacht for a honey-moon cruise. "The Lorelei." Enchanting name. A yacht! It was really too dreadful of Hugh . . .

The door opened. Mrs. Quillen popped her bluff red face into the room.

"Where's Janie?" she asked.

"I don't know," Celia answered coolly.

"I was wonderin' if she'd called the ice-man. Only this mornin' the butter was that soft ——"

Celia's foot made a tapping sound on the floor. The red face vanished. The door closed none too gently.

Butter! If only Mrs. Quillen would remember to knock! But she wasn't a servant, of course. She was a friend. If Mother were at home. Father had been removed to a sanitarium in the West. There would be another operation. It might be months before they could return to the Square. And when they did there would be the sound of a wheel chair in the hall and the gilt and green parlour would be turned into a bedroom. Celia shivered.

She stood at the window and looked down into the Square. She saw nothing lovely in the foliage of the four small mulberry trees, in the mauve plumes of the lilacs, in the new pushing green of the grass. She couldn't bear it to live here all of her life. Of what use would Hugh's money be or her own fragile beauty if she must stay in Mulberry Square?

Hugh! She saw him, at that moment, walking down the Tracy's steps, a twin clinging fast to each hand, fat sticky children with round moon faces and noses that were always moist. She saw him toss them into his car, fancied she heard through the open window their excited squeals. Father had used to do that with the children in the mill district, take them riding, buy them peppermint sticks. There was something about Hugh which reminded her of Father. Father was a darling, of course, but he hadn't had time to make Mother's life amusing. Celia couldn't quite see herself sitting in the old brick house while Hugh devoted his time to Shantytown and the regions of outer darkness beyond the railroad tracks. It was fantastic and absurd.

She wondered why she had become engaged to him. A dozen reasons, creditable to Celia, presented themselves. She overlooked the fact that she had been piqued at Carter Shelby's indifference, that she had fancied Muriel was gloating over her that rainy day last September when she had taken Carter for tea at Aunt Lucy's.

She told herself that it was because Hugh had loved her greatly and she had pitied him. She recalled the promises he had made as they sat together in that ridiculous car in the scented intimacy of a narrow side road. His ardor had thrilled her, had restored her wounded pride. His promises were peep-holes into a dazzling future. There had been a moon, glinting down through the arching trees, lying in patterns of silver across the hard dirt road. It was the night before Janie had returned to college. If she could possibly have foreseen . . .

The hurdy-gurdy was playing a familiar waltz. Celia identified the tune with a sudden swift lifting of spirits. She had danced to it with Carter Shelby on New Year's day at "Sportsman's Hall." She hummed the words softly . . . "Come with me where moon-beams . . ."

Carter Shelby! He had told her that he would do anything to make her happy. If she should go to him and say simply, "I'm very unhappy, Carter. My engagement was a mistake," would he take her away to those far lovely places which he had so beautifully described? She thought that he would. Her hand crept up to the hollow of her throat . . . "A kiss for remembrance." "My lovely lost Celia" . . . How sad he had been! He had written to her . . .

Celia unlocked the drawer of her desk and took out half a dozen of the square gray envelopes. Seating herself at the dressing table she read them through very carefully. They were casual enough . . . "Celia, dear." "Faithfully, Carter" . . . Faithfully! Here and there were unfinished phrases, a hint of sadness, a note of regret. Celia read between the lines all that she wanted to be there. Her capacity for self-deception was enormous.

She saw in the triple mirror a lovely plaintive Celia, a Celia who was triplets, each lovelier and more plaintive than the other. Thoughts slipped rapidly through her mind. Fate, she decided, was turning the handle of the hurdy-gurdy. All at once the three shadow Celias nodded their golden heads. The real Celia, after weeks of toying with an idea, had made a final decision. She glanced at her watch. One o'clock! She could take the 2:20 into the city and make connections with the Washington Express.

She had made up her mind and she did not waver. As she bathed, she assured herself that that she was doing the best thing for everybody concerned. Mother would understand. It was her dearest wish that Celia might escape the Square. Father would be satisfied if he knew she was happy. He wanted them to be happy. Dear Father! She would send him books and an inlaid chess board and baskets of beautiful fruit. Hugh would be terribly hurt but she thought he rather deserved it. And Janie, dear little Janie —— Well, Janie could never understand.

Celia dressed swiftly, selecting the prettiest of the undergarments Louise had sent her for Christmas. There was her last year's spring suit, a delicate gray with the egg-shell blouse embroidered in touches of lilac and rose. There were the suede slippers with cut-steel buckles. They were rubbed but she thought they would do. There was the soft lilac hat that always had been becoming, the woolly gray top-coat and her scarf of platinum fox. Mother had saved out of the house-keeping money to buy her that delicate scarf. Mother would never have to save out of the house-keeping money again.

She decided to take no luggage. Her suede bag would hold a nightgown, her tooth brush, her lip stick and powder and rouge. Luggage would pro-

voke questions. It was better to get away quietly.
She could send later for her clothes. She hadn't
much money. Enough to buy a ticket to Washington. She wondered idly if Aunt Lucy and Muriel
were at home.

Ready at last, she inspected herself in the wardrobe mirror. For last year's clothes she thought
that the effect was rather good. The shadows under
her eyes were a fainter lilac than the brim of the
soft felt hat. She tried to see herself as Carter
would see her; saw, instead, reflected in the mirror,
Janie's grave little face peeping in through the opening door. Celia was startled. That, she told herself, was absurd. Janie didn't know.

"Where are you going?" Janie asked.

Celia turned. Janie wore a rough little brown
wool suit and an orange beret that matched her
scarf.

"Where are *you* going?" she countered.

"Out to Aunt Rhoda's," Janie answered. "Ellen
has tonsilitis. I promised I'd read to her. Where
are you going, Celia?"

"In town," she said casually. "I have an errand
or two." And then because Janie was a dear little
thing in her orange beret and her square-toed oxfords and her rough woolen suit, Celia crossed to
her with a swift rush, held her close for a moment,
lightly kissed her cheek.

Janie's eyes, under the orange beret, widened with
surprise.

"What made that happen?" she asked.

"You're cute, Janie," Celia said gently. "That orange tam is becoming."

She regretted her impulsive gesture. Janie carried away with her a wondering expression. Celia heard the sturdy oxfords clumping down the stairs; heard, a moment later, the front door open and close. She stood at the window and watched Janie cross the street into the Square, a small figure with her hands tucked into the pockets of her coat. Celia's eyes were misty. She did love Janie. Some time she would do something very nice for the funny brown little girl.

Should she leave a note for Hugh? What should it be? She couldn't say flatly that she refused to live in Mulberry Square. She had never said that. She didn't quite dare to write that she was going to marry Carter Shelby. She decided not to leave a note. It seemed a shame. She could have done it so nicely. Her engagement ring? She opened the tiny plush case. It twinkled at her from its nest of satin. She left it on the dresser. She left it with much regret. It was a beautiful ring.

Before she left the room, she tore the flap off one of the square gray envelopes. It was marked, in his own writing, with Carter's initials and his Washington address. She tucked it into her bag and, fully equipped for conquest, she closed the door behind her.

The last time! she thought as she walked down

the wide polished stairs. She worked up a feeling
of sentiment for the old brick house. She succeeded very well. There were tears on her lashes
when she closed the front door.

The last time! Because she might not see them
again, the nymphs on the fountain were suddenly
dear. She bade them a silent farewell. She broke
a leaf from one of the mulberry trees and crushed
it in her hand. It made a stain on her pale gray
gloves. She dropped it indignantly.

Great-uncle Charlie was standing beside the ticket
window in the station. Great-uncle Charlie had felt
the uneasy magic of spring. He wore a carnation
in the lapel of his rusty swallow-tailed coat.

"Little trip, Celia?" he asked, sweeping off with
a gallant gesture his dilapidated felt hat.

"I'm going in town." She wished that he wouldn't
make her so conspicuous. People were smiling.
Uncle Charlie was a dreadful old man. She opened
her bag. The flap from the gray envelope fluttered
down to the floor. She did not notice it. She asked
for a ticket to Philadelphia.

"You are spring herself, my dear," Great-uncle
Charlie said gallantly and in a very loud voice.
"Sunshine with a hidden chill. A charming and
whimsical lady."

Celia snatched her ticket and fled. The train was
rumbling into the station.

Great-uncle Charlie saw the flap of the gray envelope. He picked it up. Because it matched Celia's

costume, he thought that she might have dropped
it. It didn't look important. He slipped it into
his pocket and thought nothing more about it. He
said good-bye to his friend the ticket-agent, tipped
his hat at a rakish angle and bounced out into the
sunshine.

II

Celia walked confidently through the Washington
station. People turned to look after her. It gave
her a feeling of power. She bought a small bunch
of violets at the flower stand and pinned them
against her scarf in front of the wash-room mirror.
She dusted her face with powder. She used a lip
stick lightly.

"What a beautiful girl!" she heard a voice exclaim.

"*Is* it Marilyn Miller?" a younger voice asked
in a thrilling whisper.

The pleased dreamy expression crept into Celia's
eyes. She smiled faintly. Her manner was detached. Inside she was simmering with excitement.
If you were beautiful, you could take what you
wanted from life.

She discovered that the flap from Carter's gray
envelope was not in her bag. It didn't matter very
much. She consulted the telephone directory.
There was his name. Carter Valentine Shelby . . .
Mrs. Carter Shelby. The Charleston Shelbys, of

course. Lovely little thing . . . Her fingers trembled as she dropped a nickel into the telephone slot.
The moment of waiting seemed very long. A voice
at last. Carter's voice, low and thrilling. His
South Carolina accent.

"This is Celia, Carter." She steadied her voice
with an effort.

"Who?"

"Celia." She was annoyed. He should have
recognized her voice.

"Oh . . ." Only that. A moment of hesitation.
Celia felt that her knees were growing weak.

"I just thought I'd call you," she said. "I happened to be in town. Can you meet me somewhere?"

"I'm leaving at midnight." Another hesitation.
"But wait . . . I'll meet you." He named a hotel.
Celia's knees were steady again. He would meet her
in half an hour.

It was a rather shabby hotel in an undistinguished
street. When she had paid the taxi-driver, there
was very little money left in her dainty suede bag.
She sat in a chair in the lobby and was annoyed with
Carter. Surely, she thought, he might have suggested a more glamorous meeting-place. For the
first time a devil of doubt scampered through her
mind. A man across the lobby was staring at her
admiringly. The devil of doubt scampered away.
She was confident again.

The moments dragged by. She glanced up expectantly with every whirl of the revolving door. At last she saw him, tall and graceful and dark, hurrying to meet her, making all the other men in the lobby look thick and dull and uninteresting.

"Celia!" He was smiling down at her, holding both of her hands. Was there a hint of apprehension in his eyes? She preferred to think there was not.

"It's lovely to see you, Carter." The silver harp strings were singing.

"When did you arrive?"

"At seven."

"Have you had dinner?"

"No." She was hungry. She hadn't thought of it before.

The dining-room was dingy. There was a great deal of plush and tarnished gilt scroll-work. There was a lamp on the table, a lamp with a pink silk shade. Carter gave an order. Celia removed her gloves, rested her elbows on the table, her chin on her folded hands. She smiled at Carter through a pink blur of light. He was looking at her hands.

"You haven't ——" He paused. She knew that he had missed her engagement ring.

"I've been very unhappy," she said plaintively. "I found I had made a mistake."

There was no hint in his eyes of the joy she had anticipated. The devil of doubt and his fifteen brothers were scampering through her mind. An uncomfortable silence fell upon them. The waiter brought an assortment of food. Celia ate without tasting. She found it difficult to swallow.

"Why are you here?" Carter was smoking a great many cigarettes.

"I've been unhappy," she said slowly. "I had to get away."

He looked at her strangely.

"Mrs. Grove and Muriel are in Ashville," he said.

"Oh . . ."

"Celia . . ."

She looked up at him quickly. She fancied his voice had an edge.

"Did you come—to see me?" he asked.

All the careful speeches she had prepared abruptly left her mind. She saw that he was annoyed. Her nails, under cover of the cloth, bit into the palm of her hand.

"Of course not," she said lightly. "I thought Aunt Lucy was home."

"The servants are there," he said. "Mr. Grove goes back and forth."

She hated him for suggesting the servants. He wanted to dispose of her. But she must not let him see that she cared.

"I'll stay with Mary Lou Miller." She had invented the name. She saw the relief in his eyes.

"A friend of Muriel's?" He wanted to be further reassured.

"A girl I met at boarding school." She smiled but she felt a little sick.

The relief in his eyes again. He had expected that she would make a scene. Perhaps there had been in his life many hysterical ladies making scenes. She knew very little about him except that he was disturbingly handsome.

"I have something to tell you, Celia." He leaned toward her over the table. "Muriel and I are engaged. I am leaving for Ashville at midnight."

She was furiously angry. She knew that anger was not becoming. She controlled her face with an effort. Her nails bit deeper into the palm of her hand.

"Muriel hadn't told us," she said evenly. She bit into a macaroon. It tasted like sawdust and glue.

"The engagement will be announced when the Groves return to Washington," Carter said, at ease now because she was taking it calmly. "Mr. Grove is pulling wires to get me a diplomatic appointment. Muriel thinks it will be amusing to live abroad."

Carter and Muriel living abroad. She couldn't bear it! Her hand, released from the biting nails, tore at the frills on her blouse. She must not let him know that she cared.

"I hope you will be very happy," she said.

"Thank you, Celia." He looked at her through the mist of shaded pink light. His eyes softened. "You are lovely," he said.

Her hand fell away from the frill of her blouse. It pleased her to think that whenever he looked at Muriel across a table he would be seeing Celia as she was to-night with the knot of violets pinned against her scarf. She was able, through the diminishing surge of anger, to feel a little sorry for him.

"I understand," she said gently. She wore her "Saint Cecelia" expression. She ate another macaroon.

She still felt sorry for him as they walked, half an hour later, through the ornate lobby and out into the mild spring night. Carter called a cab.

"What address, Celia?" he asked.

"I'll tell him." She settled back against the upholstery. A passing cab stopped for a moment beside the cab which Carter had called. Celia caught a brief glimpse of a profile that looked familiar. Before she could be sure, the cab had passed and was gone.

"Good-bye, Celia."

"Good-bye, Carter."

She ripped the violets from her coat and dropped them into his hand.

"For remembrance," she said.

The gesture supported her through the last additional good-byes. It was only when he had disappeared that she crumpled up on the wide empty seat and wept.

"Where to, Miss?" the driver asked again.

She gave him Aunt Lucy's address.

"What shall I do now?" she asked herself as the taxi threaded its way through the traffic. "What shall I do now?"

III

Celia lay in Muriel's bed and gave herself over to tears. It was a beautiful bed and a beautiful room. Even in the depths of grief and disappointment Celia was faintly consoled by the luxury of her surroundings. She saw herself reflected in a paneled mirror, a lovely languishing Celia drooping like a broken lily against the sheer lacy pillows. She wished that Carter Shelby might see her. She turned on a second bulb in the bed-side lamp the better to see herself.

Maggie came into the room preceded by a decorous knock. Maggie once had been Muriel's nurse and was now Aunt Lucy's housekeeper. Maggie was ample and kindly and shrewd. She brought a silver pot on a tray, a cup as fragile as a painted egg shell, a plate of sweetened crackers.

"Somethin' hot will make you sleep, Miss Celia." Maggie, accompanied by a rustling sound of silk and starch and petticoats, fitted a bed table over Celia's knees and arranged the pillows behind her head.

"I couldn't eat anything," Celia said with a smothered sob. "I'm simply wretched, Maggie."

"I had Hobson wire Miss Janie." Maggie

poured thick creamy chocolate into the fragile cup. "She's probably been worried." Maggie's expression was not unmixed with disapproval. She had known Celia since she was a baby. She considered her, for all that she looked like an angel, a selfish designing minx.

"I've been so unhappy." Celia lifted misty eyes. She had to be approved of—even by plain old Maggie. "I felt that I must get away."

"We've all been grieved about the Doctor. A kinder man never lived." Maggie pulled a chair beside the bed and settled herself for conversation. "To have a thing like this happen to him makes you doubt the wisdom of Providence." She peered at Celia sharply over the rims of her glasses. "You do look tuckered out," she grudgingly conceded.

"I've been simply wretched." Celia sipped the chocolate as though it were a beaker of hemlock. It was creamy and not too sweet. It tasted very good. "Will you let me stay for a few days, Maggie? I just want to lie here and rest."

"I don't know as you'd be very comfortable," Maggie answered guardedly. "The men are comin' in the mornin' to start in makin' a mess. We'll be in heaps and piles. Miss Lucy is havin' the whole house done over for the weddin'."

The wedding! Celia considered. She must pretend that she didn't know.

"The wedding?" she asked with a pretty start of surprise.

"I guess there's no harm in my tellin' you now." Maggie folded her hands against her starched white apron. "Miss Muriel is goin' to marry that young Shelby."

"Really?" Celia set the cup in the saucer. She was afraid that she might spill a tell-tale drop on the soft satin quilt.

"Mister Frank wasn't too well pleased at first." Maggie discussed family affairs with the freedom permissible in an old and valued servant. "But this Shelby has a way with him for all he's as poor as Job's turkey."

"Poor!" This time Celia's start of surprise was not affected. "I thought ——" she faltered. "Aunt Rose said that his family was prominent in Charleston society."

"Mebby so," Maggie admitted. "They're as poor as church mice just the same. Miss Muriel visited them a few weeks ago. She told me about the grand old house that's simply fallin' to pieces. His mother lives there and two aunts and an old uncle. Miss Muriel says they'd starve before they'd sell an inch of the ground or one of the silver spoons. False pride, I call it."

As poor as church mice! Falling to pieces. They'd starve before . . . The phrases were jumbling together in Celia's mind. This was a picture of Carter which she had never seen before.

"Miss Muriel made Mister Frank promise to restore the old place. I suppose now he'll have the

whole tribe on his hands. He's gettin' this young
Shelby a job in one of these foreign embassies.
Mister Frank thinks the world of Miss Muriel.
He'd buy her the moon if he could. Miss Lucy's
well pleased. I think she had an idea Miss Muriel
had set her heart on Tom McAllister. He's worth
ten of this young Shelby, if you want my opinion
about it. But handsome eyes have a way of their
own and, goodness knows, Miss Muriel will never
be pinched for money."

Celia thought over what Maggie had told her
long after Maggie was gone. Carter was as poor
as Job's turkey. It was Uncle Frank's money, the
money that Muriel would have. Celia's confidence
returned her belief in the power of her own beauty.
She saw Carter, now, as a noble young man who
had loved her too much to ask her to share his
poverty. Poor Carter! Poor Muriel! She must
never let Muriel know that her own lovely image
was forever enshrined in Carter's heart. She felt
that, after all, perhaps everything had happened
for the best.

No one must know that she had seen Carter to-
night. She couldn't bear it if anyone should know.
She thought of Hugh. Perhaps they had better be
married at once—before Muriel's wedding which
would certainly put to shame anything that could
be managed in Mulberry Square. Hugh wouldn't
insist on living in the old brick house. He would
build her a home at the far end of Manor street.

She saw it in fancy, a small perfect house, set like a jewel in graded lawns. Hugh, if he persisted in being stubborn, could help Father just as well. She would give small perfect dinners in her small perfect house. Hugh was a dear, gentle, reliable, nice-looking. He adored her.

She worked up a feeling of tenderness for Hugh, lying there in Muriel's bed with the scented spring air blowing in through the open windows. She was glad that she hadn't left a message. She pictured him frantic at her sudden departure, pacing the floor with that anxious expression in his eyes. She thought she would call him on the 'phone. Acting at once on this impulse, she pulled the lamp cord and reached for the enameled telephone by the bed.

As she waited for the operator to call, she thought with increasing tenderness of Hugh. She fancied his relief when he should hear her voice. She would be gentle and affectionate. Dear Hugh!

It was Mrs. Quillen who answered the call. No mistaking that hearty bluff voice. Celia, was it? They had received a telegram. No, Doctor Kennedy wasn't there. Nor Janie either. They'd gone out together just after office hours. To Mister Charlie Ballard's. She'd sent Johnny there with the telegram but she had opened it first . . .

They had gone to Uncle Charlie. Celia clicked the receiver into its hook. They weren't distracted about her. They were probably playing cards with that dreadful old man and drinking ginger beer and having a very nice time. Janie liked such peculiar people. So, indeed, did Hugh. Celia pulled the lamp cord and lay in the dark thinking of many things.

Janie and Hugh! Did Hugh like Janie in other than just a teasing brotherly way? The thought was absurd. Janie was a child. She did tag around after Hugh. It was really noticeable the way the child waited for him and ran when he whistled. She'd done that with Father, though. It was just Janie's way.

Celia dismissed the thought from her mind. Before she went to sleep, however, she reached a certain decision. She would not stay here for a few days, however pleasant it might be to be lazy and luxurious. She shouldn't have left Janie alone. To-morrow, on an early train, she would return to Mulberry Square.

❦ VI ❦

I

GREAT-UNCLE CHARLIE sat in what, in the days of Great-aunt Rose, had been the drawing-room of the corner house in the Square, surrounded by the souvenirs of a gay and jovial life. Great-aunt Rose, after the death of her husband, had, for a time, shared the house with him. When the shadows of the mill stacks had fallen across the Square, she had fled to a suite in the old Dauphin hotel where she queened it over other bereft ladies of aristocratic ancestry who lived in single rooms. Great-uncle Charlie had borne her deflection with admirable courage. On the evening after the last of her band-boxes, her sacred jim-cracks and Victorian relics had been transferred to the hotel, he had opened a bottle, propped his feet on a love-seat upholstered in old rose damask and indulged himself in the singing of various forbidden ditties, highly spiced and extremely gratifying.

There was little of the genteel atmosphere which Great-aunt Rose had maintained left in the long narrow room with its marble grate, its mirrors

wreathed in cupids, its floor-length windows shut-
tered with Venetian blinds. The love-seat and the
chairs which matched were tattered as to upholstery
and shaky as to frames. One by one the prisms had
dropped away from the crystal chandelier. The
carpet where garlands of roses once had bloomed
against a background of silver green was worn, in
places, down to the dingy threads. Great-uncle
Charlie's souvenirs had washed in a flood from the
upper regions and effectually obliterated all traces
of Great-aunt Rose.

Curios of a frivolous nature, from every part of
the world, crowded each other for space. There
were photographs of ladies in bustles and ladies in
tights and ladies in feather-plumed hats; mementos
of the days when Great-uncle Charlie, dapper and
gallant, had flitted from flower to flower. Old Jeff,
himself, was a souvenir of a month of revelry in
Havana when Great-uncle Charlie was twenty-two
and slim as a rapier blade. Jeff had been won, on
the turn of a card, from a dashing young Spanish
grandee. Great-uncle Charlie had been, in his time,
a gentleman of parts.

The days of revelry had long ago vanished and
gone. The "Black Sheep" of the Ballard clan was
reduced to scanty fare and the company of a few
old cronies of jovial disposition. It troubled him
not at all. Great-uncle Charlie had spent his sub-
stance in riotous living and hadn't a single regret.

As he sat, to-night, in an easy chair beneath a

sputtering gas lamp, Great-uncle Charlie was not thinking of youthful revels or of the lovely ladies he once had known, though the uneasy magic of spring came in with the fragrance of lilacs through the windows which Jeff had opened. His plump old hands held a letter which he had received a week ago and had reread many times. It was a letter from his nephew, John, and contained important news.

> *Rock Hill Sanitarium*
> *April 27—*

Dear Uncle Charlie,

In a week or so there is to be another operation. Meuller, the German surgeon, is coming to visit the chief surgeon here. They were classmates in Berlin and I am to reap the benefit of their friendship. Meuller knows more about paralysis caused by spine disorders than any man alive. We have some little confidence that the operation will be successful.

The girls are not to know. It might only raise false hopes. I don't want them to be disappointed again. We shall say nothing of the matter to Rhoda or Lucy or Aunt Rose. I knew you would be interested and, which is more important, that you won't talk about it. Helen sends her love . . .

Great-uncle Charlie smiled at that. He thought it extremely unlikely that Helen had sent her love.

He passed on to a consideration of what would happen if the operation should be a success. Uncle Charlie had kept closely in touch with the progress of events in the old brick house. He knew very well that his pretty grand-niece did not look forward with pleasure to the prospect of living in Mulberry Square. He liked Hugh, though he thought the boy was taking the matter too seriously. Uncle Charlie had never heard all the story but he suspected that Celia had, somehow, been to blame.

He knew, too, that Janie loved Hugh with all the intensity of her honest little heart. He was the only member of the family, apparently, who realized that sometime during this past year Janie had grown up. But then, with the exception of her father, no one ever thought very much about Janie. Celia was the important one. It had been that way ever since they were children.

Great-uncle Charlie was fond of Janie. He had never believed in the Celia myths. He had, through the years, watched Celia take things from Janie in her own sweet fashion. He was of the opinion that Celia had taken enough. If Celia thought there was a chance of her father recovering entirely, she would hold on to Hugh. If she thought that there wasn't, she might try to get out of it, somehow. And in the trying, she might go a step too far. The boy was in love with her. But he wasn't a fool. So reasoned Uncle Charlie. Doctor Ballard need not have stressed the matter of secrecy. Uncle

Charlie would not have given Celia that information for anything in the world.

He chuckled softly, folded the letter, slipped it into a wallet which held very little of anything else. His face, when Jeff entered the room a few moments later, was wreathed in a waggish smile.

"Jeff," he asked, "do I look like Mister Dan Cupid to you?"

Jeff's monkey face expressed complete bewilderment.

"Lak Mistah Dan who, suh?" he asked.

"Never mind, never mind." The old man laughed all over. "I don't suppose you've ever met him. Used to be a friend of mine." His blue eyes twinkled at the ladies in bustles and the ladies in tights and the ladies in feather-plumed hats. "There are friends you lose as your chins increase. Old Dan is that sort of a chap. Ah, well-a-day!" He drew a lugubrious sigh. "Get out the cards and the table. We'll do our best to forget."

That means of forgetting was, for the moment, denied them. The front door suddenly opened and Janie projected herself into the room with the speed of a whizzing rocket. Hugh followed close at her heels.

"Uncle Charlie!" Janie cried. "Celia hasn't come home!"

"Celia, eh?" The old man pricked up his ears.

"She said she was going in town. But I didn't think she would stay this long. She didn't come on the 8:15 because Stoney went to the station. I don't know what to do."

Janie talked in breathless gasps. Hugh said nothing at all. He stood in the open doorway, a question in his eyes.

"I can't imagine what's happened," Janie continued. "Have you seen Celia at all to-day?"

Great-uncle Charlie considered.

"Yes," he said slowly. "I saw her at the station. I was talking to Ben Winters."

"Did she tell you where she was going?" Janie's fingers were twisting together.

"She bought a ticket into town," Great-uncle Charlie said.

Hugh said nothing at all.

"Might she have gone somewhere from there?" Janie's chin quivered. "Celia is so pretty. Somebody might have ——" She could not finish the sentence. Uncle Charlie reached for her hand, drew her to the arm of his chair.

"There was an address ——" He paused, fumbled through his pockets, drew out a torn off envelope flap.

Janie gave a cry and then was very still.

"C.V.S." Uncle Charlie read the initials. He read the Washington address. "Who is it?" he asked.

Janie did not answer. She looked at Hugh.

Uncle Charlie looked at them both and drew his own conclusions. A mischievous sparkle danced in his bright blue eyes. His voice, however, was almost judicially grave.

"Who is it, Janie?" he asked again.

"It—it's Carter Shelby, I think."

"Hmmm . . . I see." Great-uncle Charlie saw a great deal. "Shelby, eh? The chap Celia met at the shore. Well, well, well." Each "Well" was an accusation. Janie felt that and so, she thought, did Hugh.

"But Celia wouldn't," she faltered. "Celia wouldn't ——" She knew in her heart that Celia would. She knew that Celia would do anything to escape from the Square. She wanted to say it. She couldn't, somehow. Hugh, standing there in the doorway, was looking at her so strangely.

An uncomfortable silence filled the room. Presently it was broken by the apologetic jingle of the old-fashioned front door-bell. Jeff went to investigate. He returned with a telegram.

"Fo' Miss Janie," he announced. "Miz Quillen done open it already. Johnny say hit's fum Miss Celia."

Janie's fingers trembled as she drew out the yellow sheet. She read the message and an expression of relief flashed into her eyes.

"Celia is at Aunt Lucy's," she said. "Maggie sent this. That's queer," she added, as though she were thinking aloud.

"What's queer?" Great-uncle Charlie asked.

"It's queer that Celia would go to Washington just to see Maggie. She must have known that Aunt Lucy and Muriel were in Ashville. Muriel sent me ——" She paused abruptly. A pink flush stained her cheeks. She couldn't look up at Hugh. She watched her fingers pleating the sheet of yellow paper.

"She's safe enough, anyway," Uncle Charlie said comfortably. "And now that you're here, we might as well have a party. Get out the card-table, Jeff. We'll have a game of fan-tan."

"I don't think we'd better," Janie objected, thinking that Hugh would want to get away.

"Why not?" Hugh asked quickly. "Mrs. Quillen knows where to find me if I'm needed. Come on, young fellow, I feel lucky to-night."

She knew that he didn't feel lucky. She knew that he felt unhappy and hurt. But she offered no further objection.

Uncle Charlie exerted himself to be especially entertaining. His good-humor was contagious. Hugh appeared to have not a single worry or care. Janie was soon laughing, too, excited, interested in the game. At times, stealing quick glances at Hugh, she saw that the brightness had faded away from his eyes. Once or twice she saw his jaw muscles knot into lumps and his lips close tight in a resolute line. Then her spirits drooped and there was a hurt in her heart because he was unhappy.

Great-uncle Charlie, too, watched Hugh in sly darting glances.

"We shall see what we shall see," he said to himself. "The boy isn't entirely a fool."

II

"Let's walk through the Square," Hugh suggested as Uncle Charlie's door closed behind them and they breathed in the fragrance of the mild Spring-scented night.

Janie gave a murmur of acquiescence. Hugh tucked her hand into the curve of his arm and held it there with his hand. They walked slowly across the street into the Square and under the leafing locusts.

"Spring has a lovely smell," Janie sniffed ecstatically.

"Great," Hugh agreed and was silent again.

Janie decided that silence was best. She wondered what he was thinking. The shadows were thick between the scattered lights. She could not see his eyes, only his chin and the lean angle of his jaw. It was thinner than it had been when he came to the Square almost a year ago. So many things had happened to Hugh since he came to Mulberry Square. If his father could have foreseen all this, would he have wanted him to come? She thought that he would. Hugh, too, had grown up, during this past hard year. He had learned tolerance and sympathy. People liked him. He no longer was

"Father's young doctor." He was "Doctor Kennedy," now, and "the young Doc" and "Doctor Hugh."

Why couldn't Celia be satisfied to stay with Hugh in the Square? It would be lovely to travel, of course, and live in the city and have interesting people for friends. It would be lovely, too, with Hugh, right here in the Square. Janie thought she wouldn't mind living in the old brick house for the rest of her life if Hugh loved her and Father was home and they all were happy together.

Had Celia gone to see Carter Shelby? Did she know that Aunt Lucy and Muriel were away? Why must Celia do things like that? Why couldn't she always be sweet as she had been that night when they lay curled together in Mother's bed, as she had been just after Father was hurt? She hadn't remembered very long her promise to Janie that night. She wouldn't admit that Hugh was to blame because that made her to blame as well. She asked Janie not to talk about it, please, because it hurt her too much.

Was Celia ever really hurt? She was irritated by little things, like having to economize and wear last season's clothes. She was capable of being angry. But was she ever hurt so that her heart was nothing at all but an ache? Janie remembered what Father had said that day on the White Marsh creek . . . "If you couldn't feel very unhappy, you

could never feel very happy" . . . It made you feel
sorry for Celia. Poor Celia! Janie sighed.

"What was that for?" Hugh asked.

"What?"

"That enormous sigh."

"I was thinking," she said.

"So was I." He drew her to a bench where the
light sifted down from a lamp-post globe through
the foliage of the trees. "You're a dear little girl,
Janie Ballard."

Her heart beat swiftly. There was something in
his voice . . .

"You didn't want me to see the address that Celia
dropped from her bag," he continued. "Why?
Were you defending Celia?"

She hadn't thought of defending Celia.

"I didn't want you to be hurt," she confessed.

"I wondered if that was it. You're—you're fond
of me, aren't you, Janie?"

Fond of him? She felt as though all of her was
washing away from the bench. But Hugh mustn't
know. It wasn't his fault. She had done it herself. Without any encouragement she had fallen
in love with Hugh.

"Uh huh." She gravely nodded her head.

"And I'm fond of you, little fellow." His arm
curved around her. Beneath her cheek she felt the
roughness of his coat.

"You're lovely inside," he said gently. "It shines
out through your eyes."

There was something in his voice . . . But it didn't mean anything except that he was lonely and hurt and Janie happened to be there. She hushed with a stern resolve the frantic beating of her heart. She wanted Hugh to make love to her. But not like this. Not just because Celia had hurt him and Janie happened to be there.

"We'd better go home." She edged away from the gentle curve of his arm. There was a chill in the air she hadn't noticed before.

"Don't you like it here with me?"

Like it! But it didn't mean anything. Because she was trying so hard not to care, her voice, even to her, sounded husky and cross.

"It's late," said the small husky voice. "I think we had better go home."

"All right." Hugh rose at once from the bench. The something had gone from his voice.

They walked silently past the fountain where the nymphs were dancing with arms upflung, where the water in the basin held the reflection of a star and the mulberry trees, newly-leafed, whispered softly together. Hugh did not tuck Janie's hand into the curve of his arm. She felt as though he had closed a door and shut her somewhere outside.

III

"Jeff," said Great-uncle Charlie.

"Yes suh, Mistah Cha'lie," said Jeff.

"You'd better bring in the bottle."

"But you say we boun' to keep hit fo' ——"

"This is a special occasion."

The bottle, covered with cob-webs, presently appeared.

"Only one left beside this?"

"Only one lef', Mistah Cha'lie."

There was the pop of a drawn-out cork, a pleasant gurgling sound.

"Two glasses, Jeff, you rascal?"

"Well suh ——"

"Never mind. Fill 'em up."

"Mought Ah axe what am de occasion, suh?"

"It's Spring," said Great-uncle Charlie. "And things seem to be working out very well."

❧ VII ❧

I

CELIA selected a few sprays of lilies-of-the-valley from the bowl on the piano and, standing before the mirror between the front windows in the living-room, fastened them to the shoulder of her dress. Her fingers moved so clumsily that the pin pricked her thumb. She gave an exclamation of impatience at the pin and at herself. It was absurd that she should feel a little frightened because Hugh had sent Stoney to the station to meet her instead of going himself. It was ridiculous that her hands should be unsteady because Hugh, at supper, had seemed detached, because Janie had looked at her accusingly and Uncle Charlie, who had invited himself, had grinned through the meal like a dreadful old Billikin.

She told herself that they couldn't possibly know she had seen Carter Shelby in Washington. Yet the feeling of fright persisted. Not even her own lovely reflection framed in the curlicued gilt of the mirror could reassure her entirely. She switched off the ceiling lights leaving only the amber glow of the davenport lamp. Quarter of nine. Hugh would soon be through in the office. He could come to her. It was absurd to be frightened.

She seated herself on the davenport in the circle of amber light. Across the room, in the shadowy mirror, she saw her reflection, her pale yellow dress against the dull upholstery, the flowers on her shoulder, the light glinting across her hair. This was how Hugh should see her. She folded her hands in her lap and waited with mounting impatience for him to come.

The telephone in the hall rang shrilly. She heard Mrs. Quillen coming to answer it, her heavy step, the rustle of her best black silk. To Mrs. Quillen, answering the telephone was an adventure. Celia thought that she spent her time somewhere near the hall waiting for it to ring.

"Hello . . ." boomed Mrs. Quillen. "No, the doctor, poor man, is in a sanytarium . . ." Celia knew that she was likely to give details. She did—a dozen times a day . . . "Yes, it's his house." A pause and then a snort of indignation. "Well, why didn't you say so, Tom? I'll have the flat of me hand to —— It's for you, Miss Celia," she shouted into the living-room. "It's that rogue of a Tom McAllister playin' his tricks on me."

If only Mrs. Quillen would learn to bring a message quietly instead of shouting like an auctioneer. That, Celia supposed, was too much to expect. She walked out into the hall, smoothing away the faint

lines which had drawn her brows into something
less than an angelic expression. Seating herself on
the Chesterfield, she took the telephone from Mrs.
Quillen. Mrs. Quillen lingered expectantly. The
toe of Celia's slipper tapped against the floor. Mrs;
Quillen vanished in a swishing of rusty black silk

"Hello, Tom . . ."

"So you're home again," came the familiar voice
at the other end of the line. "I saw you in Washington last night."

"Did you?" Celia's hand crept up to her throat.
Then it *was* Tom's profile she had glimpsed in a
passing taxi when she was saying good-bye to Carter
in front of that shabby hotel. "Aunt Lucy wasn't
at home," she continued hurriedly. "I stayed over
night at the house with Maggie."

"Why did you go?" Tom asked.

"I've been feeling miserable." The silver harp
strings were plaintive. Had Tom told Janie or
Hugh? She had to know. "Have you seen any of
my family to-day?"

"Your secret is safe with me, pretty girl."

Pretty girl! Tom *was* rather a dear. "Thank
you for the flowers," she said. And because she
was Celia she couldn't help adding, "I'm wearing
some of them now."

"Consolation," he said.

Consolation! She didn't quite like the sound of
that. Did Tom suspect that she had gone to Wash-

ington to see Carter Shelby? There were times when she didn't like Tom at all.

"Did you know that Muriel and Carter are engaged?" she asked putting a great deal of happy enthusiasm into her voice.

"Yes . . . And I have some news."

"Are you engaged, too?" It was strange that the thought of Tom being engaged made her feel a little forlorn.

"No." He laughed. "I'm going to California."

"When?"

"In a couple of weeks. Some business for Mr. Grove. That's why I was in Washington yesterday."

"Shall you be away long?"

"About three weeks," came the answer over the wire.

"I hope you will have a very nice trip."

"Want to go with me?"

"Tom!"

"Excuse me. I was thinking aloud." There was, in his voice, that blending of tenderness and amusement which baffled Celia and intrigued her against her will. "I'm tremendously busy. I may not see you before I go. Remember what I've often told you—you aren't quite clever enough."

Celia hung up the receiver with an indignant click. Decidedly, there were times when she was fond of Tom and times when she didn't like him at all. She regretted that he had seen her with

Carter last night. But he hadn't told Janie or
Hugh . . .

She wandered restlessly up and down the hall,
paused to look at herself in the glass of a picture.
Her lovely face hovered wraith-like over birch-trees
and a vista of painted blue lake. The Spirit of the
Forest. A lady turned by enchantment into a white
birch-tree.

Janie came out from the office, Janie in a uniform
with Kiltie trotting contentedly at her heels.

"Isn't Hugh almost through?" Celia asked.

"There's one more patient," Janie answered.

Celia thought that Janie was looking at her with
too intent a gaze.

"What's the matter?" she asked quickly.

"I was wondering if you are in a good humor."

"Why Janie-dear!" Celia's eyes were reproachful. That Janie should think she was ever anything
except sweet and sympathetic.

Janie ignored the mute reproach.

"Rachel's niece is going to be a bridesmaid," she
said. "Do you mind if I give her your old leghorn
hat?"

"Of course not." Celia pictured herself in the
rôle of a Lady Bountiful, outfitting a Shantytown
bridesmaid. "Give her that old pink dress," she
added generously. "I never can wear it again."

Janie went off upstairs with the small black dog
at her heels. Celia listened, for a moment, at the
office door. She heard Hugh dismiss the last pa-

tient, heard him close the door and turn the key in
the lock. Then she returned quickly to the living-
room, seated herself on the davenport, fluttered the
pages of a magazine.

Hugh found her there a few moments later. His
face was grave. There were no pleasant laughing
crinkles around his ruddy-brown eyes.

"Celia," he asked, standing quite still in the center of the room, "why did you run away?"

"Run away?" She lifted eyes that were filled
with tender reproach. "You make it sound so—so
planned."

"Wasn't it?" He looked at her steadily.

"Planned!" She laughed as though the idea
amused her. It wasn't an entirely successful laugh.
She knew that and hurried on. "I just happened to
notice the sign for the Washington Express in
Broad street and I thought I'd surprise Aunt Lucy.
I've been feeling miserable." The silver harp
strings quivered. "You haven't been very considerate, Hugh."

He paid no attention to that.

"You knew that Muriel and Mrs. Grove were
not in Washington." It wasn't a question. He
stated it simply as a fact. "You knew they had
gone away."

"Who told you that?" It was really too bad of
Hugh to treat her as though she were a prisoner on
the witness stand and he was a district attorney.

She curbed with difficulty her mounting rage. Anger wasn't becoming.

"Does it matter?" Hugh asked wearily.

Janie had told him. Janie wasn't a dear little girl. Janie was a sneak!

"Did Janie know?" she asked gently. "She may have thought that she told me." Her manner indicated that she wouldn't accuse Janie for the world. Hugh could infer what he liked. "Come here, darling." She smoothed the davenport cushions invitingly. "You look dreadfully tired."

Hugh remained where he had been standing in the center of the room.

"We might as well get this business straightened out," he said evenly. "I know you haven't been happy, Celia. I know you haven't been happy with me. You went to Washington to see Carter Shelby."

Celia's heart thumped. A flush which she hated crept into her cheeks. She must keep cool. He was only suspecting. He didn't really know.

"Why, Hugh!" The silver harp strings were muted with reproach.

"You dropped his address from your bag." Hugh's voice was oddly impersonal. It sounded as though he was discussing a matter of no very great importance. "You had torn off the flap of an envelope. Uncle Charlie found it in the station."

Uncle Charlie! That dreadful chuckling old man!

"Carter took me out for dinner," she said lightly, "because Aunt Lucy wasn't at home. Certainly you don't mind that. You aren't medieval enough to believe that I can't have friends. That's really quaint of you, Hugh."

She saw in a flash that she had said something wrong. Hugh winced slightly. But his voice was steady enough.

"That isn't the question, Celia," he continued patiently. "The thing that matters is that you haven't been happy with me."

"I wouldn't have gone if I had known you would mind." Celia's fingers pleated the lace on her handkerchief. "But Carter is—is almost a relative. He's going to marry Muriel."

"So that's why you came back home."

There was no anger in Hugh's steady voice. Only weariness and a sort of compassion. Celia experienced a moment of utter panic. She had lost Carter. If she lost Hugh, how could she explain it in a fashion which would be flattering to herself?

"Hugh!" She crossed to him. Her hands fluttered against his coat lapels. "You're wrong, darling. You don't understand."

His arms were around her but there was no feeling in them. They were like the limp stuffed arms of a clothing store dummy.

"You loved me Hugh," she murmured, scarcely conscious that she had used the past tense.

"I loved," he said slowly, "a Celia who was never there."

She clung to him, trembling and shaken. The silver harp strings sobbed a plaintive lament. She loved him. The dear big silly, didn't he know? She would die if he ever stopped loving her. She didn't mind living in the Square. She would always be happy with Hugh. Her breath came in broken snatches. Her lips quivered. Her eyes brimmed over with tears.

She thought that he believed her. His arms seemed to tighten. How appealing she must look all teary and shaken like this! She glanced away from Hugh, saw herself in the mirror, all her wistful loveliness framed in curlicues of gilt. The picture charmed her. She could not take her eyes away.

Suddenly Hugh laughed, not the short bitter laugh of a disillusioned lover but a tolerant teasing laugh provoked by genuine amusement. She saw that he had caught her looking past him into the mirror.

"You're superb, Celia," he said. "That was a magnificent performance."

He gently detached her clinging hands, turned, walked out of the room. Celia followed him into the hall. There was a sound on the landing. Janie was coming downstairs. Celia could just see her eyes above the enormous bandbox she carried in her arms. The small black dog was frisking around her feet.

"Look out Kiltie," Celia heard Janie say. "I can't see my feet at all. Please get out of the way."

Janie must not know that anything had happened, Celia thought quickly. After all, what had happened? She slipped her arm through Hugh's, smiled up into his eyes. She would forgive him for laughing at her.

II

Something *had* happened. Hugh realized as the days grew longer and the locusts blossomed again that something definitely had happened. He told himself, at first, that his feeling for Celia had altered, that he saw her, now, not as a lovely image which he had created but as she really was, capricious, a little selfish, given to dramatizing herself.

He tried to make himself believe that it was better so. The chances for their happiness together would be greater if he realized and accepted her limitations, if he could think of her as a human being and not as something he had imagined. He made an attempt to adjust his emotions. He discovered, one evening, that he had no emotions left to be adjusted.

He came into the garden, on that particular evening, through the alley-way gate. The garden was fragrant with lilacs and the drifting petals of the apple blossoms. The night was mild and sparkling with stars. Hugh walked under the arbor, breathing in the fragrance of spring, wondering if Janie had gone to bed. She would be glad to know that old Mrs. Pope had finally given in, that Miss Ellie'* department store clerk was, at that very moment, sitting beside the couch where Miss Ellie sat, pale but radiant, about to realize a happiness long deferred. He thought he had managed that rather well. It pleased him to know that his scheme had worked. He wanted to tell Janie.

Through the foliage of the arbor he saw two figures seated beneath the catalpa tree. One of them was Celia. He heard her laugh, saw her head, a faint blur through the shadows. She was talking to Tom McAllister.

"Hello," Hugh called.

There was a stir under the catalpa tree. Celia ran across the grass to meet him.

"I was waiting for you, Hugh," she said slipping her arm through his.

"You're very much dressed up." He saw beneath her shawl the filmy ruffles of tulle.

"Tom wants us to go to the club," Celia explained.

"It's a sort of farewell party," Tom added. "I'm off to California the first of next week."

"Sorry," Hugh said. "I can't leave the house to-night. I may be called out at any time."

"Hugh!" There was a note of reproach in Celia's soft voice.

He gently pressed her hand.

"You run along with Tom," he said, "and have a very nice time."

He didn't mind Celia going with Tom. That was something to think about. He thought about it as he changed into dressing gown and slippers and switched on the reading lamp in his room. He had a new detective novel. Janie would soon return from an evening at Aunt Rhoda's. He could tell her about Miss Ellie and they would raid the ice-box for something to eat. He preferred that to dancing with Celia at the club. It was astonishing but it was true. Hugh settled himself with a contented feeling, lit a cigarette, opened the book.

There was a gentle rap at the door.

"Come in," he called, thinking that Janie had returned.

It was Celia.

"I couldn't go without you," she said.

Three months ago the fact that she had given up a party to stay at home with him would have made him very happy. To-night he was conscious of nothing more stirring than a vague irritation.

"You should have gone," he said, regretfully closing the book.

"I'd rather stay here with you." She pulled at his hands. "Come down into the living-room and talk to me."

They sat on the davenport in the circle of amber light. Celia's head rested against his shoulder. Her fragrance no longer stirred him. Something was gone forever. She talked about the house he must build for her at the far end of Manor street. Hugh tried to be enthusiastic. He did not succeed. He kissed her. He held her close. He felt nothing at all.

Janie came in from Aunt Rhoda's. She paused for a moment at the living-room door. Celia greeted her coolly. Her manner indicated that she and Hugh preferred to be alone. Hugh was annoyed. There was no reason on earth why Celia should be rude to Janie.

"Come in, young fellow," he said, thinking how nice Janie looked in her pert little orange tam. "I want to tell you about Miss Ellie and old Mrs. Pope."

Celia stiffened against his arm. Janie yawned elaborately.

"I'm tired," she said. "I'm going on up to bed."

He heard her walking up the stairs, calling to Kiltie in her husky charming voice. He wanted to talk to Janie. But Janie had gone. Celia was laying hardwood floors in the house at the far end of Manor street. Hugh said nothing at all.

"You aren't listening, Hugh."

"Of course I am."

But Celia did not believe him. She wept. She worked herself into a state of hysteria. He attempted to calm her. He finally carried her upstairs to bed. Janie came with comfort and aromatics. Hugh left her bathing Celia's brow, talking to her in soothing murmurs. He returned to his room and tried to think it out. He no longer loved pretty Celia. What was the honorable thing to do?

"Damn!" he said after a great deal of useless thinking. He switched on the reading lamp and opened the novel. His irritation presently disappeared. He read on and on through the night.

There were similar scenes in the days that followed; tears, reproaches, hints at desperate measures. Hugh tried to reason with Celia.

"You don't really care about me. You're dramatizing yourself."

She hurled the ring at him. She was furious when he picked it up and dropped it into his pocket. She curbed the fury and sank back among the davenport cushions with a broken sob.

"I'm so miserable," she wailed.

"You needn't be. You enjoy it, Celia."

"You don't understand me, Hugh."

"I am trying to. Perhaps I am very stupid. Do you want to break the engagement?"

She never gave him a definite answer. He would not break the engagement himself. They both were miserable. Celia used every trick in her well-filled bag. At times she was feverishly gay. She made engagements with half a dozen available young men. When she saw that Hugh seemed relieved, she changed her tactics. She grew wan and dejected.

There were shadows under her eyes. She ate scarcely anything at all. Hugh wondered about it until, hearing sounds in the kitchen one night, he went downstairs to find her lunching heartily on odds and ends from the ice-box. Celia did not know that he had seen her. He went back upstairs, relieved, indignant, faintly amused.

Janie would not permit him to talk to her about Celia. She seemed purposely to avoid him. She took long walks with Kiltie for company. During office hours she was amusingly professional. She spent many evenings at the rectory, at Great-uncle Charlie's, with the quarreling Mantells.

Hugh did not know that she was trying not to interfere. He did not dream that she was alternately radiant and plunged into the depths of despair because she knew that he was no longer in love with Celia. He did not know that she was attempting to adjust herself to a new situation. He thought he had offended her. Was it because he had been so drawn to her that night on the bench in the Square? Had he fallen in love with Janie? There were many questions which he could not answer in those perplexing days.

Hugh was awakened one night by a knock at the door. He found Mrs. Quillen in the hall.

"Celia is carryin' on," she said. "She wants you to fix her somethin' to make her sleep."

Mrs. Quillen wore an indignant expression. She did not enjoy being awakened in the middle of the night. Hugh's face reflected the expression. He did not enjoy Celia's scenes.

"I'll take care of her," he said brusquely. "You go back to bed."

Celia, trembling and shaken with sobs, lay in the lilac and ivory bed.

"What is it, Celia?" Hugh asked patiently.

"I'm so miserable!" Her eyes were wide and appealing. "I keep thinking, Hugh."

She began to sob. Her hands plucked at the counterpane. Her chin quivered. She gave a splendid performance.

Hugh walked abruptly out of the room. In half an hour he returned. Celia was sleeping peacefully with the moonlight falling across her face.

III

"That's a heavy load for a little girl." Hugh, standing in the lower hall watched Janie coming down the stairs with a towering armload of books. Kiltie, as usual, was frisking around her feet.

"I've found all the ones that Father likes," she said. "It is a heavy load."

"Wait a minute," Hugh called back.

"I can manage," she answered. "Kiltie, get out of my way. Call him, Hugh."

Hugh called. He whistled invitingly. The small black dog paid no attention. Janie tripped, felt herself falling amid a shower of books.

She lay quite still with her head against the edge
of the lowest step. She was stunned for only a
moment. Consciousness returned. She could feel
Kiltie's tongue lapping her cheek as though he was
sorry that he had tripped her and asked to be forgiven. Her head ached. But that was all. She
was about to open her eyes.

Then something beautiful happened. Hugh was
kneeling beside her, holding her close. There was
a wetness on her cheeks and Janie, just then, certainly was not crying.

"Darling . . . darling . . . darling . . ."

It wasn't the Chinese nightingale and it wasn't
Hugh talking to Celia in the garden. It was Hugh
talking to Janie, holding her close, crying tears on
her cheek. Janie kept very still. She was afraid
to open her eyes for fear it was only a dream.

"Open your eyes." Hugh's voice was husky and
tender. "Smile at me, sweet. I love you, Janie.
I love you so much."

Hugh was telling her that he loved her, not because he was lonely and Janie happened to be there.
Celia was somewhere in the house and Hugh was
telling her that he loved her. Perhaps she was
dreaming . . . unconscious . . . But the smell of
Hugh's coat was real enough, the ticking of the
clock, the warm rough lapping of Kiltie's tongue.
Janie held her eyelids shut . . . "Oh God," she
prayed, "please don't let it be a dream" . . .

"Are you hurt, darling?" he asked.

"I was just pretending."

"Pretending?"

She nodded.

"Why?"

"I was afraid it was only a dream."

"Then you do love me, Janie?"

She nodded again.

"I thought you didn't."

"I must be a pretty good actress."

"And I must be very stupid."

"You are," she said happily. "I love you most of all because you're so very stupid."

"Imp!"

He lifted her from the pile of books. Her head ached. But she didn't mind. It was much less painful, she thought, to have an ache in your head than to have an ache in your heart.

"I have a great deal to say," Hugh whispered as he carried her into the living-room.

"There's only one thing I want you to say."

"What is it, darling?"

"Just call me a good little egg."

❧ VIII ❧

I

CELIA waited impatiently in the shadow of the
lilac bushes beside the gate at the end of the
garden. Tom had said that he would come in half
an hour. It seemed an eternity since she had crept
quietly out into the dark. If Tom shouldn't
come . . .

There was a chill in the air. She wrapped the
old party cloak which she had snatched from the
wardrobe more closely about her, buried her chin
in the collar of soft crushed velvet. The cloak reminded her of a happier time. So often she had
emerged from it, a Celia destined to be the belle
of the party, radiant, envied, admired. What had
happened to that Celia? She was frightened, desperate. The devil of doubt and his fifteen brothers
marched in a fiendish procession through her mind.

Hugh was in love with Janie. Something had
happened this afternoon. Janie had fallen downstairs. She wore, at supper, a bandage and a blissful smile. Celia hadn't needed to be told in words.
Janie's face was enough and Hugh's expression as

265

he pushed in her chair at the table. Janie had taken
Hugh away from her. How had it happened?
How could he prefer brown little Janie? Celia's
nails bit sharp crescents into the palm of her hand.

They were sorry for her, Janie and Hugh, Mrs.
Quillen, Uncle Charlie who had happened in at
supper time. Even Rachel was sorry for Celia.
She had offered to cook her something special, an
omelette, milk-toast. Sorry for her! She couldn't
bear it. If only Mother were home! Mother
wouldn't have let her be hurt like this . . .

She had to get away. She couldn't stay on in
Mulberry Square with Father a cripple and Mother
economizing and people talking and Hugh in love
with Janie. Tom must take her away. California!
She had never travelled. Only stupid trips with
Great-aunt Rose. It might be pleasant. Tom had
always loved her. Would he take her? He must.

If he shouldn't come! She leaned over the gate
and peered down the alley dimly illuminated by the
arc-light at the corner. There was no sign of Tom's
vigorous thick-set figure, no sound of his footsteps
on the cobbles. She drew back into the shadow of
the bushes. As she touched them, they scattered
showers of dew. The grass, too, was wet. She
could feel the dampness through the thin soles of
her slippers. Perhaps she would be ill. She pictured herself lying at the point of death with Hugh
in anguished attendance. She dismissed the fancy.

It would be more pleasant to go to California with Tom.

She grew very fond of Tom as she waited for him in the shadow of the lilacs. He was, in his way, quite as good-looking as Hugh. Everyone predicted a brilliant future for Tom. Senator McAllister, Governor McAllister. The Governor's Lady. She would advance Tom's career, be a perfect hostess, entertain distinguished people . . . "He owes it all to his wife. Lovely little thing" . . .

But if Tom shouldn't come! What should she do then? She thought of living on in the old brick house, of losing her beauty, of being entirely left behind. There was Miss Anne Vernon. She had been a great beauty in her time. Now she was a forlorn spinster living in one small room at the Dauphin hotel. Things like that did happen. Celia shivered and set her teeth. It shouldn't happen to her.

There were voices in the garden. Hugh and Janie walked towards her under the arbor. Celia drew back further into the shadow of the lilacs.

"I'm going with you," Janie said as they passed very close to Celia.

"Do you feel like driving that far?"

"I'm going with you everywhere . . . always." Janie's voice was singing.

Celia felt very lonely, crouching there in the shelter of the bushes. It hurt her to see them walk together through the gate. Hugh's arm was around

Janie; her head, with its white bandage, rested against his shoulder. Janie was secure. It was Celia who was frightened, desperate. How had it happened? Plain little Janie. Pretty Celia. Everything in the world was most decidedly wrong.

She heard the engine of the car they called "Horatius." She heard it sputter and rumble out of the alley and into Juniper street. She felt lonelier than ever . . . If you are pretty you can take what you want from life . . . That theory hadn't worked out very well. What was the matter with the world?

"Celia . . ."

Tom had kept his promise. Relief surged into her heart. She brushed her face against the foliage of the lilacs. When she met Tom at the gate, there were drops of moisture on her cheeks.

"Tom!" She gave him both of her hands.

"What's the idea of having me meet you here?" He looked at her searchingly in the glow flickering in from the corner light. "I feel like Rachel's gentleman friend."

"Something has happened." The silver harp strings quivered.

"Are you consulting me professionally?" he asked in the teasing voice which Celia could never quite understand. "You're trembling, dear." The teasing vanished. There was a tenderness in his voice. "Your hands are cold."

"I'm miserable," she said brokenly.

"Tell me about it."

Celia drew a long quivering breath.

"Hugh is in love with Janie." She lifted her face, dampened with dew, wan and wistful, framed in the collar of soft crushed velvet. She wished she could see herself. She thought that she must look very appealing.

"I know that," Tom said quietly.

"So I must go away." Celia's hands crept up to her heart. "Janie is my dear little sister. Her happiness means everything in the world to me."

"Celia, Celia!"

She drew away from him. Her head lifted proudly.

"No one understands," she said in the patient voice of a martyr. "There is no one who understands."

"I understand, my dear." There was only tenderness in Tom's pleasant voice. He drew her close to him. "Of course, I understand."

His gentleness disarmed her.

"I *am* unhappy," she sobbed, knowing that with him she could not pretend. "Take me away with you. Please take me away from it all."

"Would you go with me, Celia?"

"Yes." Her eyes were wide and imploring. "You must take me. I can't stay here."

He was silent for a moment.

"Would you marry me, Celia?" he asked gravely.

"To-night?"

"To-night."

There was, just then, no thought of the future in her mind. She wanted only to get away, to climb out of this predicament with some credit to herself.

"Yes," she said. "Yes, Tom, I'll marry you . . . now . . . to-night."

She raised her lips. He kissed them gently.

"The Scotch in me tells me to let you work it out alone," he said presently.

Fear returned, a sinking sensation.

"You wouldn't, Tom?"

"I couldn't," he amended. "The Irish in me has always loved you too much."

"Then you will take me with you?"

She waited breathlessly for his answer.

"It seems like taking an unfair advantage ——"

She swayed towards him. Her hair brushed his cheek. She felt him trembling. She knew that she had won.

"Yes," he said. "I'll take you with me. I'm feeling all Irish to-night."

II

"Janie!"

Janie, roused from a pleasant dream, opened her eyes with a start. She fancied that someone had called her. Dreaming, of course. She glanced at the illumined dial of the clock. Quarter of three! She turned over, yawned, burrowed her head in the pillow.

"Janie!"

This time she sat up and listened. It wasn't a dream. Hugh was calling her. He was rapping at the door.

"Janie!"

"Yes?" she answered.

"Come to the telephone, dear."

Hugh was calling her "dear" in that tender intimate way. She forgot to wonder why someone should be telephoning for her at quarter of three in the morning. Hugh was calling her "dear"! She sat on the edge of the bed, drowsy, ecstatic, totally unconscious of the chill in the air.

"It's long distance. Hurry, dear."

She tucked her toes into tiny slippers, fastened the cord of her quilted kimono and opened the door. Hugh went downstairs with her, switching on extra lights, yawning, smiling his crinkly smile. She didn't wonder much about the telephone call. Hugh looked so funny and young and sweet with his hair tousled and his mouth opening in enormous yawns. He loved her. That was the only matter of any importance in all the world.

"Hello," she called drowsily into the transmitter. Celia's voice answered from somewhere very far away. Celia's news, somehow, did not seem tremendously exciting. Janie talked for a few min-

utes. She placed the receiver on the hook. She
glanced up at Hugh and at Mrs. Quillen who, lured
by the jangle of the telephone bell, was ponderously
descending the stairs.

"Celia is married," she said.

"Married!" Hugh echoed the word and yawned
again.

"Married!" Mrs. Quillen, supporting herself
against the newell post, contributed the only note
of excitement.

"She and Tom were just married," Janie explained. "Somewhere down in Maryland."

"The saints have mercy on his soul!" Mrs. Quillen piously exclaimed. Her expression, wreathed
in a bristling circle of crimping pins, indicated that
Tom would stand in need of mercy.

Hugh said nothing at all.

"They're leaving to-morrow for California,"
Janie added. "Celia said she left a note for me."

"Celia would." Hugh actually smiled. "Where
did she leave it?" he asked.

"Under the bowl of lilies-of-the-valley on the
piano."

"Appropriate." Hugh's smile broadened into a
grin. "Celia would," he repeated.

The note was short.

Janie-darling,
   Now that I know how matters are, there is noth-
ing left for me to do except go away. Your happi-

ness means more to me than anything else in the
world. Tom seems to need me. I shall go with
him. Don't let any thought of me sadden your
happy hours.

Celia.

"It sounds sad, doesn't it?" Janie nestled closer
to Hugh and brushed her cheek against the shoulder of his dressing gown.

"Artistically sad," Hugh said drily.

"The saints have mercy on him!" Mrs. Quillen
repeated and took herself off to bed.

There was quiet in the living-room. Janie knew
why Celia had done it. She couldn't bear that anyone should think Hugh had preferred her. She
hoped that Celia would be happy. It didn't seem
fair to Tom. But Tom, she thought, could take
care of himself. Celia could never deceive him with
her poses. It might, after all, be a very good thing
for Celia.

"What are you thinking?" Hugh asked softly.

"I don't think Tom really needs her," Janie answered. "But the Irish in him has always loved
her." She thought of the night in the garden when
she had heard Tom talking to Celia. "He was
wearing the shamrock, I guess," she added with a
smile. "He must have been Irish to-night."

"Will your father mind?" Hugh asked, stroking
with a caressing finger the peak of her brows.

"Father likes Tom," Janie answered thought-

fully. "Mother will probably be upset because of
old Thomas and all." She glanced up at him, an
anxious question in her eyes. "Do you mind,
Hugh?"

"Poor Celia!" he said gently.

The last small lingering doubt vanished forever.
Janie sighed blissfully. The question was answered.
There was peace in her heart.

✠ IX ✠

I

FATHER was coming home! That was the first thought which popped into Janie's head as she opened her eyes one morning late in June. She pattered over to the window and curled herself up on the seat. The sun was shining and the sky was a lovely blue. It had rained the night before. There was a freshness in the air. The foliage of the locusts looked newly washed; the waxy blossoms were very sweet. Down in the Square the forsythia bushes were drifts of yellow-gold and the mulberry trees seemed to sway and dance with excitement. Father was coming home! Uncle Bradford was to drive into the city to meet them. Janie hugged her pink pajama knees. Father would be home for dinner at one o'clock!

"Isn't it nice it's such a beautiful day?" she said to Hugh at breakfast.

"Great!" He swung her up from the floor and kissed her brow where the chestnut hair dipped in a peak.

"You mustn't, Hugh," she protested, liking it very much.

"Why not?"

"It isn't dignified."

"It's nice." He set her down in the chair at the head of the table behind the coffee urn. "Now, Mrs. Kennedy," he said with a crinkly smile, "you can be as dignified as you like."

The brightness faded out of her face. It was grave and very anxious.

"Don't call me that," she said, her voice catching a little.

"Don't you like the name?" Hugh pretended to be offended.

"It's a lovely name." She looked up at him with the sunshine slanting in across her hair, a brown little girl in a linen frock the color of buttercups, a brown little girl with a shining look in her wide-set hazel eyes. "Only it scares me. I'm afraid something will happen. I'm afraid it can't possibly be true."

"It is true, Janie," he said gravely. "I love you, little fellow."

Janie glanced around the familiar old dining-room bright this morning with sunshine, at Kiltie curled up on the floor beside her chair, at Mrs. Quillen puffing in with a plate of muffins, at Hugh smiling down at her with a tender expression in his ruddy brown eyes. She thought that to-day Father and

Mother were coming home. She drew a long deep breath.

"If Heaven is any nicer than this," she said in a hushed sort of voice, "I simply couldn't stand it."

The old brick house was filled all morning with a great bustling and stir. Economy, for that day at least, was thrown to the winds. Rachel, grumbling delightedly with her head tied up in a handkerchief, prepared an elaborate dinner. Mrs. Quillen swept and dusted and polished. Janie scurried about in a frenzy of excitement with the small black dog at her heels. There was only one thing to mar her happiness. It didn't seem right that Celia should be so far away. On one of her frequent trips upstairs she peeped into the cream and lilac room. She couldn't make it seem possible that Celia was married to Tom McAllister, that Celia would never be just Celia again. Celia had been a trial. But she missed her. She wished that Celia were home.

People came with offerings. It was a gala day in the Square.

"It's not much," said Mrs. Bangs, the elder, presenting a mound of a delicacy known as "Apple Float."

"It's lovely, Mrs. Bangs." Gay little laughing notes sprinkling themselves through the air. "Thank you very much."

"You may find it a trifle sweet." Mrs. Bangs lingered in the hall. "I told Annie to use twice as much sugar as the recipe calls for so you wouldn't think we was stingy."

The "Apple Float" was more than a trifle sweet. Kiltie, in the privacy of the vine-screened kitchen porch, enjoyed it very much.

All morning the doorbell rang.

"Roses, Mrs. Quillen!" Janie uncovered a box of fragrant pink blooms. "From Mrs. Leland. Did you ever see so many?"

"Every last vase in the house is full up now," worried Mrs. Quillen who was enjoying the excitement. " 'Twould seem a shame to cut them handsome stems."

"The umbrella jar!" Janie dragged it out of the hall closet, a hideous affair of mottled green china which nicely accommodated the expensive stems of Mrs. Leland's roses.

"You do beat all, Janie," Mrs. Quillen admiringly observed. "If a brass band was needed, you'd find somethin' that would do."

It was a gala day in the Square. All morning the offerings arrived. Miss Ellie brought custards baked in pottery cups. Old Thomas brought the first strawberries from his garden. Tony Silver brought an indigestible-looking cake iced with swirls of bright pink frosting. The "General" brought three geranium blooms which he had probably "borrowed" when the owner was not around.

Great-uncle Charlie brought his last bottle of sherry wine. There was an air of suppressed excitement about Great-uncle Charlie to-day. His coat tails flipped with an extra flourish. His cravat was astonishing. The waggish smile wreathed his jolly round face.

"What time do you expect them?" he asked.

"About twelve," Janie answered, wondering if it could possibly be true that Father was coming home.

"Think I'll stay," the old man said, "if I won't be a bother."

"You're never a bother." Janie embraced him warmly. She couldn't help hugging people to-day. Even the "General" had been embraced.

Hugh came in during the morning with a man who carried a box.

"What is it?" Janie asked.

"This is my present for the Doctor." Hugh smiled at her sparkling eyes. "A radio."

"You think of everything, Hugh." She clung for a moment to his arm.

"You taught me, young fellow."

The radio was installed in the room which had once been the parlour. Janie surveyed it with some satisfaction.

"It does look cheerful," she said.

"It's great," Hugh agreed.

"We'll try to make up to him for everything."

"I can, if you'll help me." He held her close. "You're a very good little egg."

"Not that," she said very softly. "Call me 'darling,' Hugh."

"Darling," he whispered with his lips against her hair.

They were lost to the rest of the world. They did not hear the front door open and close. They were totally unaware of an audience until a voice asked from the doorway:

"Can't you lavish a little of that on me?"

Celia was standing between the portieres, Celia faintly tanned from the California sun, Celia in a smart new suit and buckled slippers and a mammoth corsage of violets.

Janie ran to meet her. They clung to each other. both talking at once. Hugh was forgotten for a moment. He lit a cigarette. He said nothing at all.

"My husband had to stop at the office." Celia, before the mirror, repaired the ravages of Janie's enthusiastic greeting. "He sent me on in a taxi."

"Your husband!" Janie echoed. "It seems so strange." She searched Celia's face to see if she were really happy. She appeared to be. Celia looks like the cat that swallowed the canary, Janie thought. There are feathers all over her chin.

"We're going to be friends, Hugh?" Celia extended a slim gloved hand.

"Of course." Hugh took the hand she offered, bent to kiss her lightly on the cheek. "The tan is becoming," he said. "You look almost real."

"Tom adores beaches," Celia remarked with the wifely air of criticizing a husband in the most dulcet of tones. "He's as brown as an Indian."

"Did you know Father and Mother were coming home to-day?" Janie, to the detriment of the violets, was embracing Celia again.

"What a little cyclone you are!" Celia gently disentangled Janie's arms. "Tom knew. He simply dragged me away from California. We flew part of the distance. Tom is a masterful man."

Celia seemed to be happy. She greeted Tom prettily when he arrived half an hour later at the old brick house. Tom was obviously very proud of his beautiful wife. It was quite as obvious that he did not intend to let her rule him. His manner towards Celia was still half tender and half teasing. A good thing for Celia, Janie thought, and a blessed good thing for Tom.

There were presents from California. Celia unpacked part of her luggage in the middle of the living-room floor, luggage which was an indication of Tom's generosity. They exclaimed over the presents. They all talked at once. In the excitement, the real event of the day was temporarily overshadowed. Celia, since her first birthday, had contrived, on every occasion, to hold the center of the stage.

The clock was striking twelve when Great-uncle Charlie bounced into the room.

"They're coming," he announced with his air of suppressed excitement increased a hundredfold. "My sainted Aunt Maria! I'm glad I'm not asleep!"

There was a rush and a scramble towards the door. Mrs. Quillen in her best black silk rustled down the stairs. Rachel came out from the kitchen with a chicken ready for broiling clasped to her bosom. Great-uncle Charlie's coat-tails were flying in all directions. They gathered in the open doorway. People were assembling from all parts of the Square.

"You'd think it was Lindbergh!" Tom exclaimed.

"It's a great day in the Square," Hugh said quietly.

"I wish they'd hurry!" Celia was dancing up and down.

Janie said nothing at all. She just clung tightly to Hugh's arm, a lump in her throat, happy tears on her lashes. Father was coming home!

Uncle Bradford's car turned into the Square. It seemed an eternity before it stopped in front of the old brick house. There was Stoney on the front seat with Uncle Brad. There was Aunt Rhoda. There was Mother in a new blue hat, smiling and waving her hand. There between them was Father, thin and pale but smiling, too, and waving his hand at them.

Stoney opened the door of the car. Aunt Rhoda stepped out. Mother followed, Mother not quite so plump but pretty still and wearing a new blue coat. Stoney would have to lift Father, of course. Janie felt that she couldn't bear it to see Stoney carry Father up the steps. She hid her face against

Hugh's arm. The arm was shaking a little. She knew that Hugh was minding it dreadfully, too. She pressed her eyes tightly against the tweed of his sleeve.

"Praise Gawd!" That was Rachel's camp-meeting voice. It indicated that something of great importance had happened. Mrs. Quillen was booming. Celia was crying. Tom was exclaiming.

"Look, Janie dear," Hugh whispered in a choked-up sort of voice.

Janie lifted her eyes from his arm. They widened with surprise. A wave of happiness rushed over her which almost bore her away. Father was walking! Using a cane, leaning on Stoney's arm, Father was walking towards them, mounting the steps of the old brick house.

II

There was a great deal of confusion at dinner. No one seemed to mind that Rachel's cap frill was awry or that she had salted the berries. Mother sat behind the coffee urn and smiled tremulously. Father, in his familiar place, ate a little, sipped Uncle Charlie's sherry, embraced them all in the genial warmth of his smile. Stoney stood behind his chair and could not be persuaded to move. Mrs. Quillen hovered in the doorway. Janie left her place beside Hugh half a dozen times to perch on the arm of Father's chair and rest her cheek against his.

"I'm so happy," was all that she could say. It was quite enough. She made a song of it. Gay little laughing notes sprinkled themselves through the air.

Father smiled at Hugh.

"You won't have to make the sacrifice, my boy," he said kindly. "You can go whenever you like."

"I shall stay as long as you need me," Hugh answered in a choked sort of voice. "And when I go ——"

He looked at Janie. Everyone looked at Janie. She felt that her cheeks were flushing, that her eyes were shining like stars.

"Janie is so young," Mother objected.

"Time will take care of that." Father patted her hand. "Plans, Hugh?"

"No definite ones." Hugh still looked at Janie. "We'll go abroad for a year or two."

We! That meant Janie and Hugh. She knew it was true but it seemed like a beautiful dream.

"We'll talk about it later," Father said. "Surprised, weren't you? Uncle Charlie knew."

"But I didn't tell." The old man chuckled. He glanced at Celia. Janie glanced at Celia. Her lashes shadowed her eyes. What was she thinking? Was she happy? Her hand, lifting a goblet, trembled. Drops of water spilled down on the cloth. Mother looked at her anxiously.

"What are your plans, darling?" she asked. "Where are you going to live?"

"Tom hasn't told me," Celia answered, twisting the stem of the goblet. "He says it's a surprise."

Tom calmly threw a bomb into the family circle.

"Mr. Grove has sold me the 'Governor's House',"
he said.

Celia lifted startled eyes.

"You're going to live here in the Square?"
Mother's voice was incredulous.

"Of course." Tom leaned back in his chair.
"These are the people who will support me when
I break into politics. This is where I shall live."

"That's a good idea." Father smiled his approval. He liked Tom. He thought that he would
succeed. "We'll keep one of them here, Helen,"
he added, reaching down the table to pat Celia's
hand. "I consider it a great idea."

Uncle Charlie chuckled. Mother looked distressed. Celia said nothing at all.

"Besides," Tom continued, "that house, for
years, has been my favorite dream. The Governor's
House."

"You'll probably make the title authentic," Father said. "You'll probably get there, Tom."

"Thank you, sir." Tom expected to make the
title authentic. There was a confidence about him.
Mother brightened. Celia's lashes lifted. Great-
uncle Charlie made gallant amends.

"To the Governor's Lady!" The old man lifted
his goblet and smiled his waggish smile.

They made a ceremony of drinking the toast. Celia was very gay. Janie wondered what she was thinking.

She knew, after dinner, when she heard Mother and Celia talking upstairs in Celia's room. Celia was weeping. Mother was attempting to soothe her. Janie, who had meant to enter the room, paused outside the door.

"It's a fine old house," Mother said, "and very attractive inside."

"But this Square, Mother."

"I know, dear." Mother sighed.

"There's no use coaxing Tom," Celia said plaintively. "He does exactly as he pleases."

"He isn't unkind to you, darling?" Mother asked quickly.

"Not exactly," Celia admitted. "But he's as stubborn as a mule. It's very hard to bear."

"Why did you do it, Celia?" Mother, by wire, by mail and in person had asked that question a hundred times.

"Do you think I would stand in Janie's way?" Celia murmured reproachfully.

"Of course not, dear." Mother said proudly. "You are always generous and kind. Aunt Rose wrote me that it was brave but very foolish of you to make such a sacrifice. She's going to give you a complete set of flat silver."

"Is she?" Celia, Janie thought, was forgetting

to be plaintive. "I want the same pattern as Muriel's. Do you think she will get it, Mother?"

"I'm sure she will," Mother answered. "Aunt Rose understands."

"I wanted to do what was best." The silver harp strings were muted. "Janie's happiness means a great deal to me."

"I've always said," Mother murmured tearfully, "that you have a sweet disposition."

Janie's left eyebrow cocked itself whimsically. She couldn't feel angry at Celia. There was no room for resentment in her happy heart. She curled herself up in the window seat and fell to dreaming, wide-awake dreams, which, miraculously, were real.

"Janie wouldn't have minded staying," Celia said presently. "It's strange that she should be the one to go."

"I don't understand it, Celia." Mother never understood anything that she didn't want to believe. "I don't understand it at all."

Janie didn't understand it either. It was amazing that Hugh should love her. She fell into wide-awake dreams which, miraculously, were true. It had been an eventful year. But the hard times were over now. Mother was at home. Father was taking a nap in his own room down the hall. At any moment, Hugh might be calling her to ride with him out into the country. It seemed like a beautiful dream.

She wanted Celia to be happy. She sounded happier now. She and Mother were making plans to go to Washington for Muriel's wedding.

"Poor Muriel!" Janie heard Celia say with a note of complacency in her voice. "She has always loved Tom."

"And Carter Shelby really wasn't ——" Mother hesitated.

"I'd rather not talk about it, please."

Janie knew that Mother would always believe that Carter Shelby had been rejected because he had failed to measure up to Celia's high ideals. That was just as well. It would make Mother feel a little superior to Aunt Lucy. People were amusing. Janie sighed and smiled.

Tom presently came up the steps with a square white box in his hand.

"Where's my wife?" he asked.

"You like to say that, don't you?" Janie teased.

"It makes me feel important."

Celia met him at the door of the lilac and ivory room. She kissed him prettily. Tom presented the box.

"For the Governor's Lady," he said.

"Thank you, dear."

Celia assumed an imposing manner. She wasn't unhappy, Janie thought. Celia could never be very unhappy. She was playing the Governor's Lady and Tom was faintly amused.

"Janie!"

That was Hugh!

III

It was quiet under the mulberry trees. The hurdy-gurdy had trundled itself away. The children had gone and the shabby old men who sat at night in the Square. Only the nymphs on the fountain were left, silver spangled, dancing with arms upflung.

They sat on a bench near the fountain, Janie and Hugh, with the mulberry leaves, rough and heart-shaped and silver-lined rustling softly above their heads.

"It's like the night we sat here a year ago," Hugh said.

"Only very much nicer." Janie nestled close beside him. Her hand slipped into his. "I shouldn't have dared to do this—a year ago."

"Did you want to, little fellow?"

"I liked you," she confessed.

"And I liked you."

"You hated Mulberry Square."

"I don't hate it now . . . Do you remember that I told you I had found right here the loveliest thing in life?"

She remembered distinctly.

"But you didn't mean me," she said.

"I think I always meant you," Hugh said thoughtfully. "You have all the qualities that I tried to find in Celia."

They were silent for an interval. The mulberry

trees whispered quietly together. The nymphs on the fountain looked as lovely as they could. The locusts scattered their fragrant blossoms. The tipsy old lamp-posts tried to stand up straight. They all knew Janie. She was a favorite in the Square.

"Hugh," she said presently.

"Yes, darling?"

"There's one thing that bothers me very much."

"What is it, little fellow?"

"You might be disappointed some time. You might be sorry . . ."

He tilted her chin, smiled at the solemn expression on her grave little pointed face.

"There isn't much to you," he said softly, "except your hazel eyes and your lovely smile and your courage and your loyalty. I love you. I think I can make them do."

THE END